A Journey in Roman Catholicism

A Theological Novel

Richard P. Belcher

ISBN 1-883265-25-8

Richbarry Press

P.O. Box 302 Columbia, S.C. 29202

Printed in the United States of America

An Introduction to the Journey Series

This book is the eleventh in a continuing series about Ira F. Pointer and his struggles to understand and defend the truth of the Word of God. For the reader's help, a summary of each book is given in this appendix.

Book One, *A Journey in Grace*, finds Ira in college in the fall of 1970 studying for the ministry in Collegetown. His theological pursuit in the book becomes Calvinism---what is it, and does the Bible teach it? As the book unfolds, he becomes pastor of Lime Creek Baptist Church, and then moves to First Baptist Church of Collegetown. At the end of the book, he marries Terry Lynn Lasitor during the Christmas season of 1971.

Book Two, *A Journey in Purity*, begins in the winter of 1971, and Ira faces the problem of impurity in the lives of his church members in First Baptist Church. This forces him to pursue the subject of church discipline, which in turn, brings a great upheaval in the church. It is during this time of friction in the church, that Dink, a gang career criminal, is saved, and he soon becomes Ira's best friend.

Book Three, *A Journey in Authority*, is set in the year of 1972, a few months after book two. Ira is in a new church, Unity Baptist Church, which was planted when the issues at First Baptist Church could not be resolved. The theological search this time concerns church government---elder leadership versus congregational rule.

Book Four, *A Journey in the Spirit*, has its setting in the spring of 1973. Ira is still at Unity Baptist Church, but comes in contact with Durwood Girvin, the new pastor at First Baptist Church. Because they are at odds on the subject of the Holy Spirit, Ira searches the Scripture to determine its witness on this important subject.

Book Five, *A Journey in Inspiration*, finds its setting in the summer of 1976, as Ira has finished college, but now heads off to seminary in Seminary City, while still pastoring Unity Baptist Church. At seminary he is unintentionally caught up in the inerrancy battle, and finds out again that standing for the truth is difficult and costly.

Book Six, *A Journey in Providence*, begins five years later in 1981. By that time Ira has finished a Master of Divinity degree, and is taking a rest before pursuit of further studies. He is still pastor of Unity Baptist Church. The book begins with the kidnapping of Dink's son, which results in Ira and Dink studying the providence of God in the book of Job, as they search for Dink's son.

Book Seven, *A Journey in Eschatology*, originates during the summer of 1982, when Ira faces a double challenge---to find his birth parents and to write a book at the insistence of a friend on the subject of eschatology. Both pursuits prove to be much more difficult than he had anticipated.

Book Eight, *A Journey in Salvation*, commences during the fall of 1983, and Ira by this time has joined the faculty of Evangelistic Baptist Theological Seminary in Seminary City, where he is teaching and also pursuing doctoral studies. The theological search centers on the doctrine of salvation, as Ira and Dink seek to help a fallen pastor, Jasper Showers, understand the basics of that area of truth..

Book Nine is titled *A Journey in Revival---True or False?*, and is set in the Spring of 1985. By this time Ira has completed his doctoral work, and is still teaching theology at the seminary. He is drawn into this theological conflict by a challenge from one of his students. As the book unfolds, he seeks to persuade several that the end-time revival, in which they have become entrapped, is not Biblical.

Book Ten is titled *A Journey in Baptism*. Ira and one of his students, a Presbyterian pastor, discuss objectively the doctrine of baptism. Ira sets forth a covenantal Baptist view, and the student presents the Paedobaptist understanding of baptism. At the same time, Ira is pulled into a puzzling sniper mystery, which baffles even Dink.

Book Eleven is titled *A Journey in Roman Catholicism*. Someone frames Ira of having written a book indicating he will become a Roman Catholic, which creates a stir at the Baptist seminary where he teaches. Ira and Dink pursue the mystery of who framed him and why, as he also prepares another book concerning why he could never become a Roman Catholic.

Though each book is part of a series, a person can read any book separately with understanding, as each plot stands independently of the others, and each theological study is independent as well. However, some characters from the previous books appear in later books as part of the plot and are noted in footnotes.

Who Could Have Done This?

Have you ever been falsely accused of something you did not do? No big deal, if it is a small matter! But what if it was of such magnitude that it brought the demand that you resign from your job, immediately, and leave your present position with some shame and disgrace? And to make it worse, suppose you were being framed, and the evidence stacked against you would have convinced even your own mind, if you had not been the accused, and knew you were not guilty of such a deed! But maybe I had better start at the beginning of this story---unbelievable even to me now as I think back on all that took place as a result of this one false accusation.

Yes, I am speaking of my journey in Roman Catholicism, and it all began in the fall of 1986. By this date, as many of you as regular readers know, I had settled into the role of a theology professor at Evangelistic Baptist Theological Seminary in Seminary City, having taught there since 1983. By now I was thirty-three years old and was beginning to think I would probably spend the rest of my life in my present position. And then it happened!

I was told via a phone message from my Dean of Faculty to make an appointment to see him immediately. Such calls are not unusual in an academic setting, except that this one was not from the Dean's secretary, but from the Dean himself. I gave that fact no second thought, as I concluded that his secretary was probably tied up with something else. I must admit now, as I think back on the

2---A Journey in Roman Catholicism

situation, the Dean's voice did sound a little strained and serious---more so than usual.

When I returned his call to make that appointment, the Dean's secretary answered, and I then came to know that the matter must be serious, since he wanted to see me that very day! I agreed to meet him at 3:00 in the afternoon, after my last scheduled class. I could not begin to anticipate even remotely what would be the subject of our conversation or the result of it.

When I walked into his office, I expected the normal wait for him to finish his previous appointment, but to my surprise I was ushered immediately into our meeting. As I studied the situation, I noted that Dean Harbour did not have his usual friendly backslapping spirit and attitude, nor did he joust with me in his friendly conversational mood even for a second. He got right to the point! I was hardly seated before he thrust a book into my lap and demanded, "Did you write this book?"

With great shock at his attitude and demeanor, I quickly turned the book over so I could see the cover, and sure enough the author was listed as Ira F. Pointer! But that was not the real shocker---the title of the book just about took my breath away, and it certainly left me speechless. The book was titled *Why I Am Going to Become a Roman Catholic*.

As I perused the cover, I noted it had a picture of me on the back, as well as a biographical sketch of my life and ministry---and whoever wrote it gave evidence of knowing me rather well. I was absolutely shocked! I thought surely there had been some mistake here!

I looked back at the Dean and smiled, which may not have been the right thing to do at this moment, and I said in my befuddled voice, "You've got to be kidding!"

He was not open to smiles or explanations or laughter.

"Dr. Pointer, I am not kidding! We have talked to the publisher, and have done a thorough investigation of this matter, and there is no other conclusion we can reach, except that you are the author of this book!"

For many readers I need not explain the Dean's attitude and concern about my writing such a book as this. It is well known that Baptists and Roman Catholics do not have very much in common in their theology, and the last thing an evangelical Baptist seminary would want on their faculty would be a man who was a closet Roman Catholic.

But now I was beginning to get a little aggravated at his accusation. Surely his attitude was wrong---as well as his conclusions! He had me tarred and feathered without giving me any opportunity to defend myself.

"Dr. Harbour, I don't know what kind of a thorough investigation you have done, or what convincing evidence you have, which would lead you to conclude that I am the author of this book. But I state emphatically to you that I did not write this book, nor do I have any knowledge of who did! I think you owe me the courtesy of backing me and giving me a chance to clear myself of these charges, before you go riding off into the arena of battle over a false accusation!"

My denial did not satisfy him, as he then issued his ultimatum.

"Dr. Pointer, either you resign from your position immediately, or you will be fired immediately. I have already discussed this with the President of our school, and with the Chairman of our Board of Trustees, and this is their decision also."

My reply did not make him happy, but I gave it and then left immediately.

"Dean Harbour, I will not resign---you will have to fire me, because I know that I did not write this book, and if given enough time to make a thorough investigation of this matter, I could prove you wrong---for I am innocent! I do not understand how you can call a man into your office and demand a resignation without giving him an opportunity to answer your accusations. You say you have made a thorough investigation of this situation, and maybe you have. But I assure you that whatever you have done in trying to get to the bottom of this mystery, your conclusion is wrong. If your information seemed strong enough to convince the whole world of my guilt, and I was the only man alive who knew the truth, I would still argue my innocence, because I know something no one else knows! I know that I did not write this book! I am not going to become a Roman Catholic! And I may write another book and tell you why! And I am not going to resign!"

Do You Know Me?

As I left Dean Harbour's office with a copy of the book that I had supposedly written, I tried to walk and read at the same time, which was not easy, since I was totally consumed with the latter but not the former---walking, that is. I brushed several people, who must have wondered what was wrong with me, and I probably ignored several others who spoke to me along the way. By the time I got to my office, I was fuming. Someone was trying to frame me. All the evidence pointed to the conclusion that I was the author of a book that I had not even seen before, let alone authored. Clearly, someone was trying to frame me---just to get me fired from my teaching job at the seminary. But who and why?

I sat down at my desk and began to look for the name of the publisher of the book, and there it was---Garland Press of Seminary City. I had never heard of them nor seen them before in the city, as I had driven around town, but I noted that they were located at 259 Bartlett Street, which I knew was in the downtown area. Still fuming, I left my office for the parking lot with book in hand to go and confront whomever I found at that address. It was probably not the best time to stare someone down on any subject, and God was gracious to intervene in my plans, as I ran into Dink,[1] as he was pulling into the driveway of the school parking lot.

"Hey, Preacha, where ya goin' sa fast?" he inquired.

"Dink, you'll never believe it!" I said ignoring his question.

"Never believe what, Preacha?" he inquired.

"Dean Harbour has demanded that I resign, because someone has framed me! And if I don't resign, I will be fired!" I said still fuming over the whole situation.

"Whoa, Preacha! Slow down a second, an cool yer heels! Ya still ain't answered mah question. Where's ya goin' an fer what?" he asked again.

By then I was calming down---some. So we both parked and I explained it all to him, and then asked him what he thought I should do.

"Well, der's nothin wrong wid goin' down der jus' ta look round a bit, but ya gotta be careful whatcha say," he instructed. "Ya never know what's youse gettin' inta, so ya gots ta play it cool!"

I agreed to his suggestion, and even told him I would keep quiet as we paid our visit, and let him ask questions of whoever was there. I was much calmer (but still eager to face the publisher), as we drove the several miles to the downtown area, and sure enough there was Garland Press on Bartlett Street. Dink pulled up in front of the establishment, which was one of several businesses which stood side by side in that area of town. We got out of the car, and I saw, as we approached the door, that there was only one man in the sales area of the business. We walked in intending only to survey the place and ask some casual questions. I had the book, but it was well hidden, and would only be revealed as necessary in our conversation.

We looked at some of the books, which this publisher had in the shelves near the door, as the man behind the counter finished a phone conversation. We remained in our browsing mode, waiting for him to come to us. Sure enough, when the phone call was finished, he began walking toward us, but what a surprise when he spoke.

"Why, hello, Dr. Pointer! How are you today, and what can I do for you? You'll be eager to know that your new book is doing quite well on the market!"

I forgot all about letting Dink do the talking!

"What? Sir, do you know me?" I asked.

"Why, yes, you're Dr. Pointer, and you teach theology out at Evangelistic Baptist Theological Seminary. We just published your book on Roman Catholic theology. Why, you and I have talked dozens of times in getting your book printed and on the market!"

"Sir, I don't mean to shock you, but I have never seen you before or talked to you before in my life, and I certainly did not write this book!" I said, as I pulled the book out from under my jacket.

I was calmed down now, as the original disgust and shock had worn off, and I was thinking clearly enough to look closely at his reply. Either he was part of the scam, or someone had scammed him also.

"Oh, come now, Dr. Pointer! We have a signed contract with you. You brought that book to us about six months ago. I would know you anywhere! For the life of me, I don't know why you would say these things!"

"Well, then just let me see the contract!" I said with a rather matter-of-fact attitude, confident that my signature was not on any such document as that!

To my surprise he readily agreed, and he slipped into the back part of the building to get it. I felt quite confident he had no such document! But to my surprise, within a minute he reappeared carrying a file, and as he walked he pulled out a piece of paper.

"Here it is!" he noted, trying to be friendly. "It is signed, sealed and now delivered."

I had expected to find an obviously unidentifiable signature, as far as any similarity to mine, or at least a poor forged substitute at best, but to my surprise and shock---it was either my signature or an expert forgery. I showed it to Dink, and he was as flabbergasted as I was, because he knew my signature very well. Now was the time for more questions.

"How long have you been in business here?" I asked.

"We've been here for about ten years!" he replied with some protest in his voice. "Dr. Pointer, how can you say you did not sign this? I was present when you did so, and you were so excited to get the book finished and published. I wondered what a professor at a Baptist College was doing writing a book telling the world that he was going to become a Roman Catholic and why, but I figured that was your business, not mine."

And then he became stern in his attitude!

"Look, if you have changed your mind, and want to accuse us of publishing a book you never approved, you can't get away with that. I'll fight you in court and beat you! I have several witnesses---a secretary, and other workers here who will quickly identify you!" he said.

"You would have no objections submitting my signature to an expert for analysis?" I queried.

He never answered that question, and convinced that I had said enough, and maybe too much, I left not knowing why he gave me no answer. Had I gone too far in my accusations, or did he know my signature was a forgery?

Dink shook his head as we left and commented, "Preacha, if I didn't know ya, I'd tink you was goin crazy! Dis case is gonna be a tough one ta crack!---maybe da toughest one we'se faced! An I'se gots no idea where ta begin ta try ta solve it."

I appreciated Dink's honesty, but that left me even more perturbed. Where could we begin our investigation? What was I to do while the seminary was making their demand for me to resign? If I once resigned, would I ever be able to clear my name and prove my innocence? Would any other school hire me if this case seemed so conclusive concerning my guilt?

As Dink and I drove the few miles back to school, we took shelter again in the one truth we could not deny---that our God was working all things after the counsel of His own will (Ephesians 1:11). Thus, as much as we did not understand, we could understand that truth. Our God had made no mistake in all these unfolding events which so puzzled us. We were assured in our hearts that God would be glorified in some way in this matter, even if the world never did understand or believe the truth.

What mattered the staining of my name or reputation before men, if God knew the truth? What mattered my suffering and loss of reputation or job or even life, if God were glorified in the events before us? We agreed that would be our attitude and comfort as we labored together to get to the bottom of this mystery! Little did we realize how hard the enemy would seek to break us, even through friends. The battle was just beginning!

---

[1]Dink has been Ira's best friend since the second journey book, *A Journey in Purity*, when he was converted out of the background of a Mafia type environment. He possesses a "street savvy," whereby they together have solved numerous mysteries in the other journey books.

3

Why Won't You Resign?

When we had finished praying and turning the matter over completely to the Lord, I concluded it was time to summarize what had taken place in the last few hours.

1. I had been accused of writing a book, which I had not written, and on a very controversial subject, supposedly presenting a viewpoint with which I did not agree.

2. I had been shown a contract with my name and signature on it, which I had never signed nor seen before.

3. I had met a publisher, who had printed the book, and who seemed to know me well, but whom I had never met before.

4. I had been asked to resign my position as a theology professor at the seminary immediately or be fired without any opportunity of defense.

5. I had concluded that someone was doing a professional job of framing me in order to get me fired from the seminary for some reason.

6. I concluded that we (Dink and I) had to think of who might do such a thing, so we could begin to investigate and get to the bottom of the whole matter.

As I discussed it further with Dink, a smile came over both our faces at the same time. And our voices echoed the same name!

"Todd Shelton!"

Or, if known by his alias, Girvin Othneil Durwood![1]

He was an End Times Evangelist (also an old college friend of mine) whom I had exposed as a fraud in the Spring of 1985. Fuming and spewing hatred and revenge against me, he had then vanished into thin air (not even the police had been able to find him), and he had not been heard from since. But before he left, he had threatened to destroy my ministry at the seminary, as he thought I had destroyed his as an evangelist.

But how could he have orchestrated this series of events? Were the publishers in cahoots with him? Were they frauds too? Would they intentionally be doing his dirty work? Could he have perfected my signature? All of those things seemed to be genuine possibilities, but what about his ability to look like me, if the publishers were honest men? Did I have an imposter walking around somewhere, who had perfected my speech and handwriting? It seemed impossible to even consider. But if it wasn't Todd, who was it?

Dink and I batted around these possibilities as we sat in my office. Our problem was that time was short, and an investigation like this might take several weeks. Then Dink made what seemed to me to be a very viable suggestion.

"Preacha, whys doncha resign under protest an wid da stipulation dat if youse can prove yer innocence, den da seminary has ta restore ya ta yer position?"

That certainly sounded fair to me, but would it be agreeable with the seminary? We decided to go directly to Dean Harbour's office and present the terms of my resignation, which we did, but only after I had written my letter of resignation with these terms clearly spelled out. I must say when we walked into his office, and presented the terms of resignation, we caught Dean Harbour by complete surprise. I guess he thought that I was definitely and undeniably guilty, and that the exposure would bring an immediate resignation. He did not expect an innocent plea, or a protest of the school's demands.

"Dr. Pointer, I cannot act on these terms of your resignation. I must speak to the president first, and he may have to take the matter to the board of trustees. You would make it much easier on us all, if you would make a clear break and confession of this matter, and give a full resignation."

"Even if I am innocent?" I asked.

Again, my answer shocked him!

"Well, I can't promise anything, but I will speak to the president. But again, it would be much easier on all of us, including you, if you just admitted what you have done and then resigned from your position!"

I wondered if I needed to put my question on a large piece of cardboard, so I could hold it up for him to see.

"Even if I am innocent?" I asked again.

But I added something else for good measure.

"Would you plead guilty to something you had not done, just to settle the matter for the satisfaction of other people? Do you value your reputation so little that you would let someone smear it and frame you for something you had not done, just to satisfy the request of people who do not believe you are innocent?"

Then came an agreement and a threat!

"Dr. Pointer, the president of this seminary has put this matter in my hands to solve. I am going to accept your terms of resignation. But let me tell you in no uncertain words, that if you cannot prove your innocence within a reasonable time span, you will never teach again--- anywhere! I will see to that!"

Then he added the clincher, which I had thought about, but had not mentioned to Dink.

"And, you, Dr. Dink, if you side with Dr. Pointer on this, you will be asked to turn in your resignation also!"

Yes, Dink was on the faculty at the seminary also, as the professor of evangelism, and his humble heart and demeanor, combined with his shrewd toughness, plus those very street smarts, had made him very popular with the students. No one could deny that he had the gift of evangelism (he was always witnessing to someone with unbelievable genuine results). Nor could they deny his brilliance, even though he still talked like a gangster. Through the years, at times, some with great arrogance had made sport of his speech and mental abilities, but they had always lived to regret it, as he had out-maneuvered them with a very humble response, as they sought to attack and embarrass him.

Dink replied to the Dean's threat as if he was way ahead of the Dean on the matter, which he probably was.

"Well, sir," Dink began, "ders no need fer me ta wait fer ya ta ask me ta resign, cause I can tell ya right know, I'm goin ta be on Dr. Pointer's side, tryin' ta help him prove his innocence. So, Dr. Dean [that's what he called Dean Harbour], ya jist as well take dis letter in ta yer secertary an tell her ta type out a copy wid my name on it, so's I can sign it right now!"

Dr. Harbour's mouth dropped! It was obvious that he had not expected this either. He knew that the student body might be able to take one of us resigning, but both of us?

Reluctantly, Dr. Harbour exited with my resignation in hand, and in about three to four minutes he came back into the room with a copy for Dink to sign, which he did. His head was hanging low, and grief was written all over his face. But Dink was not finished.

"Now, Dr. Dean, let's just get dis straight! We is dismissed from teachin' any of our classes? Right?"

The Dean nodded in agreement.

"An we's free to pursue Dr. Pointer's innocence?"

"An when we's proven Dr. Pointer's innocence, we'll both be reinstated ta teach agin---here at dis seminary?"

Nods came each time Dink asked a question.

"An when we's proven Dr. Pointer's innocence, all back pay will be made up ta us?"

"Yes, yes, all of those things are in the agreement!" Dr. Harbour admitted. "But can I ask you men something?"

He seemed to be worried now about the reaction to what had just taken place.

"Can we just keep this to ourselves?" he almost pled.

I smiled and asked, "What will you tell people when we are gone tomorrow from classes? What can we tell people who ask us why we are no longer teaching? What happens when this accusation filters through the student body? Don't you think it would have been better for you to stand with us, than to demand a resignation, when there is the definite possibility that I may be innocent, and this thing will fly back in your face with unpredictable results?"

He never answered! And though we felt sorry for him, we had work to do. But where would we begin to try to come to grips with the answer to this mystery?

----

[1] See *A Journey in Revival*, by the same author, published by Richbarry Press.

How Many Strikes Do We Get?

After leaving the dean's office, we decided that the place to begin our investigation was to seek to determine what had ever happened to Todd Shelton, my old college friend and roommate. Seeing he was the only suspect we could come up with, that seemed to be a logical place to begin. So when back in my office (I wondered how long they would let me use it), Dink got on the phone to try to locate our good friend, Mac Turnover, who was the owner and head of Turnover News Agency, one of the largest in the world.[1]

While I waited for him to get some information, I began leafing through the book which I was supposed to have written. I noted the many reasons the author had given for desiring to become a Roman Catholic. The following were his arguments, not mine.

1. The Roman Catholic Church has a glorious history going all the way back to Christ.

2. The Roman Catholic Church can claim the Apostle Peter as its first Pope.

3. The Roman Catholic Church is the only authoritative interpreter of the Bible.

4. The Roman Catholic Church is the dispenser of the grace and merits of the work of Christ.

5. The Roman Catholic Pope is Christ's representative on earth today---the successor to Peter.

6. The Roman Catholic Church possesses and administers all the glorious sacraments. Christ intended for His church.

7. The Roman Catholic Church's worship is the most magnificent and impressive of all the professed churches of the world, including its music, ceremonies, etc.

8. The Roman Catholic Church has a size and an influence and a respect and a beauty, which surpasses all other clerical bodies of the world.

9. The Roman Catholic Church has the greatest array of holy men and women (saints) of the past of any other church body of the world today.

10. The Roman Catholic Church not only is able to dispense the grace of Christ, while men are alive in this world, but it is also authorized to dispense His grace beyond the grave to those who have died and not gone directly to heaven.

I was so engrossed in these claims that I didn't notice Dink motioning me to the phone to talk to Mac Turnover. After Mac heard my problem (which obviously shocked him as well), he promised that he would get on the matter of locating Todd Shelton immediately. But then suddenly Mac put one of his reporters on the line to speak to me.

"Dr. Pointer, I overheard the conversation concerning your search for Todd Shelton!"

My answer of "yes," encouraged him to continue.

"Well, he supposedly died several months ago. It was one of the strangest cases I have ever seen. It seems that he withdrew all the funds from his end-time ministry association (millions they say), and then he got on a small plane he had chartered and flew it into a mountain out in the Rockies. There was such an explosion, when the plane hit the mountain, and the terrain was so rugged and impossible to explore, that it never could be determined if he had remained on board till the plane crashed and disintegrated in the explosion and fire. It is known that there was a parachute on the plane, so some speculated he might have bailed out with the money somewhere over a wooded area just prior to the crash. But there is no evidence whatsoever of that, even though men have searched and searched."

"Well, so much for that hoped-for lead!" I commented.

When I got off the phone and told Dink these things, he replied, "Sounds like old D. B. Cooper ta me!"

"Who is D. B. Cooper?" I asked with great interest.

"Oh, he's some guy dat bailed outa some commercial plane out west somewheres, an dey never found him! But dey did find some of da monies on da ground!"

With some disappointment, I asked Dink, "Well, where do we begin to look for the guy that framed me now?"

"Beats me, Preacha!"

---

[1]See *A Journey in Inspiration*, where Ira first meets Mac Turnover as an adversary, but through Ira's witness he gets saved. See also *A Journey in Revival*, where Mac comes to Ira's aid and helps to rescue him from a previous false accusation.

How Does One Explain the Differences?

I didn't feel quite like going home yet, so I sat and continued to think about Roman Catholicism and the book, which falsely bore my name. I leafed through the pages again, and reread the various areas listed as strengths of the Roman Catholic Church. As I turned the subject over in my mind, I was smitten with the stark contrast between those characteristics and the characteristics of the apostolic church. I began to make a chart as follows:

**A COMPARISON OF THE APOSTOLIC CHURCH
ACCORDING TO THE NEW TESTAMENT
AND
THE ROMAN CATHOLIC CHURCH
AT THE TIME OF THE REFORMATION**

The Church at the Time of the Apostles	The RC Church at the Time of the Reformation
1 Simple worship	1. Elaborate liturgy
2. House churches	2. Elaborate expensive cathedrals
3. Elder leadership in each church---no pope mentioned in the Bible	3. An elaborate hierarchy over all the churches including a pope, etc.

4. Authority---Scripture alone	4. Authority---Scripture plus tradition church councils papal encyclicals, etc.
5. Salvation by faith alone	5. Salvation through the Roman Catholic Church
6. Salvation by faith alone in Jesus Christ by the grace of God alone	6. Salvation by Christ's merits distributed only by the church based on man's works
7. No salvation apart from Jesus Christ	7. No salvation apart from the church
8. A spiritual kingdom entered by faith---a kingdom not of this world---a kingdom not to rule the world in its present state	8. An earthly kingdom (the Roman Catholic Church) which is ordained by God to rule this world during its present history
9. Mary---the mother of Jesus	9. Mary---the mother of God and a co-redeemer with Christ
10. Every believer a priest ---no magic men or rites	10. An elaborate priesthood with supernatural rites and sacraments and priests to offer Christ continually as a sacrifice

11. Two ordinances with no saving power in them	11. Seven sacraments with saving power in them
12. Sees a clear and proper distinction between the OT and NT	12. Fails to see a clear and proper distinction between the OT and NT and therefore there is the continuation of priests and sacrifices in the NT period

When I finished this simple chart, I noted several obvious questions that needed to be answered.

1. How and why did the apostolic church move so far from what it was in its beginning---almost opposites in many areas?

2. Were these changes in history acceptable to God or was there a time in history when such major changes disqualified the resultant Roman Catholic Church from being a New Testament church according to Scripture?

I concluded that we could look at the problem by means of a chart showing a level time line. The early church was on that time line, because it was established by Christ and the apostles. But at some time in history the church began to depart from the characteristics of the early church, noted by the downward line. But at the same time, there is the revelation in the Scriptures concerning what the church should have been, represented by the broken line which continues on the same plane as the early church and represents what the church should have continued to be.

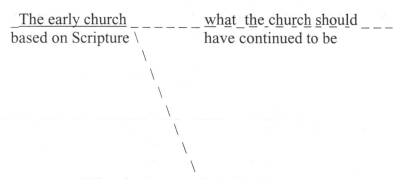

The early church _ _ _ _ _ _ what the church should _ _ _
based on Scripture \   have continued to be
                      \
                        \
                          \
                            \
                              \
                                \
                                  \
         What the Roman Catholic Church came to be
         in the development of Christianity in history

I well understood how the Roman Catholic Church prided itself, because it thought it could trace itself back through history to Christ (which it cannot do). But after looking at this chart and thinking for awhile, I concluded that the question is not which church can trace itself back through history, but which church has the characteristics of the early New Testament apostolic church.

For example, if I have an authoritative description, say of a cat, then I do not have to be able to trace that cat back to its original ancestor to prove it is a cat. I merely have to compare the cat before me today with the authoritative description of a cat to make the determination one way or another.

Similarly, if I have an authoritative description of what the church should be (and I do have such a description in the New Testament), I do not have to trace a church back through history to prove it is Christ's church. I merely have to see if it fits the description of Christ's church as given in the New Testament. If it fits the description in the

New Testament of what the church was then and should be today, then it is Christ's church. Likewise, any group that claims to be a New Testament church today, but does not fit the description of the church given us in the New Testament, cannot claim to be His church. That goes for its doctrine and its structure. Both must be present to be a New Testament church.

Thus, that is the question we will be pursuing in the days ahead. Does the Roman Catholic Church of today possess the doctrine and the governmental structure of a true New Testament church? And can the Roman Catholic Church really trace itself back to the New Testament, though we have already admitted that this is not really the issue before us?

As I sat thinking in the dark, I then realized that I was not at the bottom of the problem even yet. The whole issue did not turn on how one views history, but it was more of an authority issue. It was the authority structure of the Roman Catholic Church which caused them to see nothing wrong with the church's changing through the centuries. And what a change did take place from what we had seen the New Testament Church to be in the apostolic era to what the Roman Catholic Church became by the time of Reformation period.

Thus, my first pursuit in looking at the comparison of the two eras (the apostolic church and the Roman Catholic Church today) was to take a deeper look at the authority structure of each one. But not just now!!! Now I had better scamper on home for supper!! So I thought!!

Won't This Evidence Clear Me?

I must admit that by the time I got home, I was extremely tired, no doubt mostly from the mental strain of the events of the day. I figured I had just about enough strength to eat supper, and then slouch into my favorite chair and drop off to sleep. But such a peaceful evening was not to be, for as soon as I sat down to rest (you guessed it), the phone rang. I was not in a very good mood when I answered with a simple hello.

"I've found the money you are looking for!" an unfamiliar voice informed me.

"What money? Who said I was looking for any money?" I asked, playing dumb.

"Don't be coy with me!" the voice answered, showing a rough edge on it. "You know what money I am talking about!"

"Who is this?" I asked, still fishing for information.

"This is the voice of a man who knows where Todd Shelton is, and what happened to him and his money!" he informed me.

"Then, tell me where he is and we will both know!" I blurted out, then wondered if I was being a little too smart.

"Where are you now, and when can I meet you?" I asked.

"I'll be in touch!" he said, which announcement was followed by an abrupt ending of the conversation.

For the next several minutes I sat stunned in my chair, trying to figure out what I should do. But then my thoughts were interrupted with anther phone call.

"Dr. Pointer! This is Mac Turnover again. I have just received information that Todd or one of his associates is in your area. My sources have traced him there to Seminary City. He has been living there for several months, though we're not sure where."

I thought at this point that things were coming together. I immediately asked Mac for this man's name and address. I was told his name was Fred Forrester, which was probably a fictitious name. I immediately called Dink to ask him to meet me at a gas station near the address. I told him I would fill him in on the details when we got there.

I tried to explain to Terry (my wife) why I had to leave immediately, and she was very understanding. She had learned by this stage of our marriage that my presence through an entire evening was not always certain!

I met Dink, and we made our way over to the address that Mac had given me, and we went to the front door of a darkened house. The door was cracked open slightly. We knocked, and when no one answered, we pushed the door open and found a light switch. No one was to be seen, so we quietly went on into the living room. Then we pressed on slowly into the other rooms. It was in the bedroom that it became apparent that whoever had just been there had made a quick exit. Dresser drawers were empty, but still open. Other things were scattered about the floor, as if someone had made a quick survey of the contents of the room, picked out some items and discarded the rest.

After we had gone through the remaining items in the bedroom, we went from room to room searching quickly but carefully (the best we could do under these circumstances) to see if we could find anything of informational value. It wasn't until I got back to the living room and opened the desk drawer that we hit the jackpot. I found a copy of the contract, which I had supposedly signed, for the publication of the book, which I had supposedly written. But more than that, we saw a stack of papers containing numerous pages where it appeared that someone had endlessly practiced copying my handwriting. Surely, this was evidence that someone had been trying to perfect my handwriting.

"What do we do now?" I asked Dink. "Do we call the police to confirm what we have found here? Or do we take the evidence to Dr. Harbour to prove my innocence?"

When Dink didn't answer, I discovered that he was in another room. Then I heard him call to me, "Preacha, look here! Deys got some pitchers a you!"

I went into the next room, took the pictures, and began to thumb through them.

"Dink, this isn't me!" I exclaimed.

"Sure looks like ya, Preacha!"

"Yes, but it's not me!" I protested.

'Den who is it? An' how does ya know it ain't you?"

"Because I don't have any clothes like that---a sweater that looks like an old high school letter sweater? And trousers that are pegged at the bottom? I haven't worn anything like that for years!" I insisted.

At this exact moment, when we thought we had some key evidence to clear me, the room shook with a gigantic explosion. I had no further thoughts till I awakened in a hospital bed with my head spinning and my vision blurred and several parts of my body aching. I did remember the explosion and concluded someone must have pulled me out of the house and rubble. But where was Dink?

Could It Be That Dink Is Gone?

As I rubbed my head and groaned, my vision focused so I could see Terry standing beside the bed.

"Where's Dink?" I demanded.

"They didn't find Dink at the scene of the explosion! He's still missing!" she explained.

"Do you mean he wasn't found in the rubble?" I asked emphatically.

"The police said you were the only one they found, when they got there!" she explained.

I started to get out of bed, but the pain was too great! And Terry was quite insistent that I not try that again---to which I readily agreed. But I did insist that she tell the police that there was another man in the house at the time of the explosion, and they needed to look for him. She got on the phone and informed someone---I wasn't exactly sure who---and within a few minutes an officer was standing over my bed wanting to know about this other man who was supposed to have been with me in the house. He assured me that I was the only one in that house when the firemen arrived.

My answer was simple, as I protested, "Then someone must have taken him out, because he was there when the explosion took place! Please, go take another look!"

He tenderly informed me that it would do no good to look again, because the house was nothing but a mess of ashes now. He added that if another man had been in the building, he must have been consumed by the fire. My mind was blurred, but I did get the full force of that statement. Dink, my best friend of several years, could be a clump of unrecognizable ashes. I began to weep! I had to conclude that someone had set us up, and had caused the explosion, just as we were in the house.

I asked the officer, "Sir, how did I get out? Why didn't I burn up also?"

With a shake of his head, he explained, "That is one of the strangest things I have ever seen. The explosion must have blown you away from the initial area of the explosion and fire, which enabled the fireman to rescue you. Your friend must have been left in the midst of the burning building. The only other way you could have escaped was to have crawled out, while you were in a state of semi-consciousness. Either way, your friend didn't make it."

Through my squinting eyes, as they were trying to focus, I asked the officer, "Isn't there another possibility?"

"Huh?" he said, announcing he hadn't thought of any other possibility.

"Could it be that someone pulled my friend out also, and then took him away with them?" I suggested.

"Why would they do something like that, and not tell us?" the officer asked.

"Because they planned this thing for revenge. And part of their revenge against me would be to make me think my best friend was dead!" I explained.

"What was the other part of the revenge?" he asked.

"They let us see the evidence we were looking for to prove my innocence, and then they destroyed it in the fire by detonating an explosion!" I explained again.

I also detailed for him the accusation that had come against me, along with all the events of the previous day. I then asked, "Don't you see? How many people do you know that lose their job and their best friend---all in one day! I will admit that the evidence was lost in the fire, according to their plan, but I refuse to admit that my friend is dead! I will find him, if it's the last thing I do in my life!"

I am sure that the officer left my room with his notebook full of information, but also with his mind filled with doubts concerning all my suspicions and thoughts.

The doctor informed me that I would probably have to stay in the hospital several days, even though I was eager to try to find Dink. I called Mac Turnover and informed him of the most recent turn of events, and urged him to see if he could find out what had become of Dink. He broke down and cried over the phone at the thought that Dink might be gone. He then promised he would not leave any stone unturned in the search for information concerning Dink and the persons who had framed me.

After the officer was gone, I asked Terry if she had been in contact with Janie, Dink's wife. My concern was how she would take this, after the loss of their two-year old son, just a few years ago![1] She said she had talked to Janie several times since the explosion, and assured me she would keep in close contact with her in the days to come.

When all the people were gone and the room was left dark and quiet in hopes that I would sleep, I poured out my heart to the Lord. The crying turned into deep and uncontrollable sobs.

---

[1]See *A Journey in Providence* published by Richbarry Press, 1999.

What Is Sola Scriptura?

I don't remember when or how I finally drifted off to sleep that night, but upon awakening I discovered that the oft-quoted statement that joy comes in the morning is not true, unless it is speaking of the resurrection day for the saints of God. I awoke about 3:00 AM, partly from the heaviness of my heart and partly due to the aches and pain of my body. I must have taken a pretty good blow to my head, when I hit the ground, after the explosion gave me a pretty good ride through the air. I knew it was too early to get up (or if such was even possible), and it was going to be too difficult to get back to sleep, so after a period of prayer and meditation, I did something else. I called for the nurse and asked her to bring me a pen and some paper (she gave me a strange look, I am sure, because of my request). I then tried to occupy my thoughts with the book which I was supposed to have written.

I was open to anything that would pass the boredom and pain of the night hours. Is there anything so useless as being awake at night, and trying to chase sleep, but never being able to catch it? How many times can you turn over in bed to try to find a more comfortable position, especially one who was in my condition?

Sola Scriptura versus a Multi-source View of Authority

I had already noted before that the initial difference between Roman Catholics and those who disagreed with them at the Reformation period was the doctrine of Sola Scriptura---Scripture alone, as the authority of the church, versus a multi-source entity as the authority of the church. The doctrine of Sola Scriptura was an easy view to explain ---Scripture only---period. The multi-source view of the Roman Catholic Church was not so easy to understand or to explain.

The Roman Catholic view would also believe in the authority of Scripture, but obviously not Scripture alone. The church must not only have a divinely inspired scripture, but it must also have a divine guardian and interpreter of Scripture. Such a divine but difficult book as the Bible cannot be left in the hands of common men to interpret. Plus, since Scripture does not speak on every subject, there must be a divine means of determining how Scripture is to be applied to our lives.

In simple words, according to Roman Catholic dogma, the church is the guardian and interpreter of Scripture. But how does that work out in a practical manner? The church is the guardian and official interpreter of Scripture and its application through the declarations of the church councils, through the statements of the popes, through the tradition of the church, etc., etc., and these statements are also as authoritative as the Scripture itself.

Thus, the common Roman Catholic Church member cannot be trusted to read and interpret Scripture for himself, but can only believe what the church tells him to believe through the total accumulation of the above authority structure. Neither can the common Roman Catholic Church member be trusted to apply the Scripture to his life, but must depend on the Roman Catholic authority structure to interpret and apply the truth from all the above sources.

Whether it be the doctrine of man, or the doctrine of salvation, or the doctrine of Mary, or how to live, one cannot go to Scripture alone to find the answer. One must go to the totality of all the above noted accumulated material as merged and noted and interpreted by the church over its unfolding history in order to find an answer in any and all theological, doctrinal and practical matters.

Is it any wonder the cat no longer looks like a cat? That is to say, is it any wonder that the church at the Reformation no longer looked like the apostolic church? Is it any wonder there had been many additions to the church's beliefs, structure, and practices through the ages till the church no longer resembled the early church planted by Christ?

Now lest one think this settles the issue in a debate with a Roman Catholic, it does not. This is what should be expected, we are told. The church as the kingdom of God on earth is a living organism, which changes through the years as divinely guided by God, for He is the One who has set up the Roman Catholic Church and its authority structure, we are told. He is the One who in Christ said, "I will build my church and the gates of hell shall not prevail against it." He is the One who is and has been guiding and guarding His church through His appointed authority structure. He is the One who is responsible for the growth and change in the church throughout its history.

Roman Catholics say that this took place by God's appointment even in the Old Testament. They had Scripture, but Scripture was not self-explanatory. The laws and prophets needed interpretation and application. One writer says:

Even after the Books of the Bible had been gathered together the people still needed in addition to the inspired word of God found in the Old Testament, official interpretation of the meaning of the Scriptures, particularly those parts which directed them what to do, what to avoid, and how to worship God. There can be no doubt that such a system prevailed among the Jews; they were led and directed by living authority, and this living authority directed them for centuries before the written and inspired words of authors long since dead were collected into a book.[1]

The only problem with this line of argument is that if the Old Testament people of God had such an authoritative line of continuing infallible interpreters, how did they miss the coming of their Messiah? Should they not have had an authoritative interpretation of the Old Testament, which alerted them to the kind of Messiah God would send? Wouldn't they have seen from Isaiah 9 that their Messiah would be divine? Wouldn't they have seen from Isaiah 53 that their Messiah would be a suffering Messiah and that He would die? These are the two points where the Jewish expectation of their Messiah completely failed. They never concluded that He would be divine nor that He would suffer and die. Thus, either the supposed infallible interpreters failed, or such infallible interpreters never existed, contrary to the claims of the Roman Catholic Church. Either possibility would destroy the Roman Catholic contention.

But to state our argument more fully, it seems that the failure of the case, which the Roman Catholic Church tries to build for the Old Testament people of God's need of infallible interpreters, would also point to the error of their claim. We might put the matter as follows. If the claimed authoritative interpreters of Scripture in the Old Testament were neither accurate nor authoritative, how can they be used to seek to establish a necessity for such authoritative interpreters of the New Testament? Plus, if anyone would read church history as it unfolded, it should be clear that the Roman Catholic Church and its supposed pronouncements by the popes, councils, tradition, etc. were far from infallible, as is now claimed.

And could not one also draw a similarity between the coming of Christ and the coming of the Reformation? Christ came to rescue His Old Testament people from the false idea of the need of supposed infallible interpreters, which actually had led God's people into their error. The Reformation came to rescue a people from an apostate church, which had come to believe also that they were infallible, and that they alone could interpret Scripture.

Thus, in both instances the error was the same (the Scripture needs an infallible interpreter), and in both instances the reformation was the same---the church has an infallible and inerrant Scripture, which leads us to the doctrine of Sola Scriptura. Scripture alone must be the authority of God's people, not some supposed infallible interpreter or interpretation of Scripture.

And would not Christ tell us today that God has spoken in finality through His Son, the living Word, and through the Bible, His divinely inspired written Word? Should this not bring us to the Word of God with prayer and caution, as we seek to interpret the Bible, and should it not give us a reluctance to believe some supposed infallible interpreter or interpretation? Dare we allow anyone to bind our conscience to a man or to a group of men or to a church, as far as the interpretation of Scripture?

After making these notes, I settled back into my bed to rest, and immediately was hit with the reality of the day before me. Another sober thought came to me also. How could I ever solve this case without the help of Dink? I was discovering, though I knew it already, that the possible loss of anyone close to us was very difficult, not for just one reason, but for so many reasons.

---

[1]*The Bible Is Not Our Sole Guide,* Joseph E. Ritter, Imprimatur, Archbishop of St. Louis (St. Louis: Supreme Council of the Knights of Columbus), p. 11.

9

What Is Happening to Me?

I was not aware of anything further until I was rescued once again from my semi-conscious state by the delivery of a form of breakfast. I nibbled on portions of it, as my mind was becoming alert to the reality of my circumstances once again, and to the dilemma before me. I sought to summarize in my mind my situation so I could better understand what to do next.

1. Someone had gone to a lot of trouble to frame me---and it was a very convincing frame job.

2. Someone had removed my right hand man---the one who had been so central in all my previous journeys---Dink.

3. Whoever had framed me had changed his appearance so that he actually looked like me and could reproduce a signature almost identical to mine.

4. Someone had actually written a book in my name (a book containing doctrine with which I had strong disagreement), and he had published it in my name, and now it was being distributed in my name. Plus, there was no way I could stop the distribution because the publisher had what he thought was a valid signed contract.

5. Someone had used the book to try to get me fired from my teaching position at the seminary.

6. Someone had let me see the evidence which proved that it was a frame job, and then destroyed it by an explosion and a fire.

7. Someone had allowed me to be rescued from the fire, but had either kidnapped Dink or let him die in the fire.

8. That someone seems to have been my old nemesis, Todd Shelton.

I sat thinking of what Todd had said over a year ago when he blamed me for the destruction of his corrupt worldwide end-time revival ministry. He had said:

> The race is not to the swift,
>   Nor the battle to the strong,
> But to the man that nobly lives,
>   To right an unjust wrong![1]

He had gone on in his threat to admit that his first thought was to gain revenge against me through my family ---even the possibility of destroying us all. But he had concluded such would be much too quick and crude. His desire was for me to suffer as great a sorrow in the loss of my reputation and ministry as he had suffered. He promised his plan of revenge would be a masterful plan and would take some time to bring to fruition. He said he would follow me to wherever I was living to execute it, and when the time came, he would be totally unrecognizable. No part of his previous existence would allow me to recognize him, because it would all have changed. By this means, he would work from behind the scenes to destroy me. I wouldn't even know it was happening until it happened. He would destroy me professionally, just as he thought I had destroyed him. Until that day came, he wanted me to worry and fret, but all such agony would be to no avail. He guaranteed me that the hammer of God's vengeance would fall upon my head---swiftly and unexpectedly.

I could not deny it! The events of the past day had all the marks of the promised plan of revenge of Todd Shelton, alias Girvin Othneil Durwood (his end time prophet name!). Or whatever his present name might be! Could it really be that a former college roommate, one I had helped in so many ways, was actually carrying out his dastardly plan of revenge? I had helped him supposedly come to know the Lord. I had recommended him to his first church as a pastor. I had counseled him when he had gotten in trouble. I was the one who had helped him make new starts, only to see him drift away once again. I was the one who had helped him clean up so many messes he had made in his life. Could it really be that he was now trying to destroy me?

My thoughts were interrupted by a phone call from Terry. She wanted to tell me she would be by to see me early in the afternoon. That meant that I had another long stretch of hours to whittle away, so after the morning bath, I turned once again to my thoughts concerning the Roman Catholic Church.

---

[1]See *A Journey in Revival* by Richard P. Belcher, Richbarry Press, 2002, p. 195.

10

What Then Is Our Authority?

In my last thoughts about the Roman Catholic Church I had discussed their authority structure. I had seen that the Roman Catholic Church rejected the doctrine of Sola Scriptura in favor of a multi-source basis of authority, which gave the church the final say as to the understanding and interpretation and application of Scripture. I had also tried to stress that these were two entirely different authority structures (Sola Scriptura or Scripture alone versus the multi-source view of the Roman Catholics), and each one of these two views leads the group subscribing to it down a different pathway of development in its history.

A Comparison of the Two Authority Structures

The Sola Scriptura view would challenge the church to always seek to follow a Biblical pattern of doctrine and its application. That is, the church of every age must compare itself with Scripture, and seek to bring itself in line with the teaching of the Word of God, the Bible.

The Roman Catholic view of a multi-source authority structure would allow the church to change and develop through the centuries, even sometimes coming to an entirely different view of a doctrine than that of the Scriptures (as we shall see later). For you see, the Roman Catholic Church says it is not only the guardian of truth through history, but it is also the developer of truth in its authoritative tradition as well.

A Common Complaint against Sola Scriptura

One often hears the complaint that the Sola Scriptura basis of authority leads to too many different groups (denominations, etc.). But one could properly answer that objection by noting that even with some differences between the Sola Scriptura groups, there are many similarities. And it must also be admitted that in the final analysis of history, there is a mainstream of believers from various groups, who have held through history a body of major doctrines, due to their common understanding of the doctrine of Sola Scriptura. The differences between these groups in their understanding of a body of major doctrines is far, far less than the differences between the apostolic church in the first century and the Roman Catholic Church of the Reformation period or the Roman Catholic Church of the twenty-first century.   That is to say, the apostolic church or New Testament church is not even recognizable, when one looks at the Roman Catholic Church of today (see the chart in Chapter 5 of this book).

A Complaint and Not a Criticism

Now at this point, I do not offer that as a criticism, but as an observation and illustration. It is an observation and illustration of the fact that a Sola Scriptura conviction of authority for the church takes one down an entirely different road of development of the church and of supposed truth than the multi-source theory of authority as possessed by the Roman Catholic Church. Again, that is why the Roman Catholic Church differs so much from the New Testament church as revealed in the Bible.

The Two Extremes in Dealing
with the Authority of the Church

The more one thinks about this subject the more one comes to the conviction that there are two extremes in dealing with the authority of the church in a Christian's life. It is true that in a local church setting, even for those who hold to the doctrine of Sola Scriptura, members of that church are to be submissive to their leaders in that church ---the elders, pastors---call them what you will (see I Timothy 3:5, Hebrews 13:17, etc.). But does that mean a believer must submit himself or herself to those leaders regardless of what they say or teach, or only as long as they are faithful to the teaching of Scripture?

That is the tension, and we, being frail mortals, always find it easier to go to one side of a theological tension, rather than keeping the balance of the two. Side one of the tension for one holding to Sola Scriptura is the necessity of submission to the leaders of the local church---I am to be submissive to them and their authority, so says Scripture. Side Two of the tension is the Lordship of Christ over my life and my personal relationship with Him, which is often called the priesthood of every believer. It means that I have a personal responsibility for my life as well, to be obedient to Christ and His Word prior to the authority of any man or any group of men, so says Scripture.

The problem comes if and when I surrender my life unconditionally without question in every area to a group of men in a church, because even though they are appointed leaders in the church, they still are fallible men and can err. If you don't believe it, look at the many who have made that error, that is, surrendered to the authority of men, in the history of the church---both the leaders and the members of a church.

The Bible even recognizes that leaders can err. Why the necessity of all the qualification of elders in I Timothy 3? And could not the elders even though thought to be qualified prove themselves to be unqualified at worst, or be open to an error of judgment, though qualified? Do not the Scriptures say that even Peter erred and Paul had to rebuke him to his face (Galatians 2:11-14)? How then can any Christian yield absolute and unquestionable submission to any other man---even a leader or leaders of a church? Submission, yes, but absolute and unquestionable submission, no. The submission must be on the basis of that leader's submission to the authority of God as expressed in the Bible.

Overbalancing to One Side of the Tension--- The Mistake of the Roman Catholic Church

This is the mistake the Roman Catholic Church makes. It demands absolute authority of the church over their members' lives concerning spiritual matters---period! That means the church is authoritative over what one is to believe, how one is to live, whether or not one is going to heaven, etc. Has not the Roman church taken the place of the Bible and the Holy Spirit in the believer's life? Has not the Roman church overbalanced in favor of the church and its authority to the rejection of the authority of the Bible and the Lordship of Christ?

Overbalancing to the Other Side of the Tension the Mistake of Many Protestants

But one can also err by an overbalance to the other side of the tension---that is, by separating oneself completely from any involvement in a local church and its leadership and authority. This is the mistake of some Protestant groups. They are so independent that they will not listen to anyone or consider any possibility that they could be wrong in their thinking and ideas about the Bible and its interpretation. Just as a church or a group of men who are leaders in a church can come to see themselves as the only authority in spiritual and doctrinal matters, so an individual can do the same thing. That is the other side of the tension.

The Biblical Necessity of Holding
Both Sides of the Doctrinal Tension

The Biblical necessity, and here is where the tension comes, is for an individual believer to be involved in a local church and be submissive to its leaders, and yet at the same time walk under the authority of Christ's lordship and His truth as revealed in the Bible. In the process that believer must honor God's ministry to him and God's authority over him through His church and its leaders. But at the same time he must continue to walk expressing his individual priesthood as a believer, and as one who is responsible to Christ alone as his Lord and Savior.

The Scripture says that there is one mediator between God and man, and that man is Christ Jesus. I must never let any man or group of men take the place of Christ or the Holy Spirit in my life (I Timothy 2:5). That is why the great majority of Protestant churches do not have priests. The book of Hebrews makes it clear that Christ is our only priest. He is our great high priest, who not only was the one who offered up to God the sacrifice for our sin, but He also was the sacrifice, which He offered to God. He has offered the complete and final and absolutely sufficient sacrifice for sin. He is my representative before God. He is my advocate. The Old Testament priesthood was gone with the coming of Christ. There is no priesthood in the New Testament except that of Jesus Christ and the individual believer before Him.

Summary

Therefore, the New Testament believer has a dual responsibility---to walk in surrender to the Lordship of Christ and to walk in submission to the local church and its leaders, as long as they are walking in submission to Christ. Christ will always be faithful, though we must be sure we have a biblical understanding of Christ. The elders are mere men who can err. Therefore I am to be submissive to them as long as they follow Christ's Word.

Thus, walking in submission to the elders is only possible as these leaders of the church see their proper place and do their God-ordained work of the church with a godly and spiritual attitude and life. Yet, we must also recognize that it is so easy for even church leaders to want to become lords over other men, even in His church (I Peter 4:3).

But, again, on the other side of the tension, this precarious balance is only possible as I am willing to take my place as an individual believer under the Lordship of Christ, and refuse to allow men for convenience sake or due to my laziness to become lords over me.

It must be admitted that it is much easier but improper and unscriptural to move to either side of the tension. We must carefully, for our own sake and the sake of Christ's church, maintain the delicate balance between the two. Thus, the members have a clear obligation, as do the leaders of the church, as we must admit that both could err!

As I was mulling over these matters, the phone in my room began in its usual manner to demand that I answer it. Nonchalantly I did answer it, but my lazy demeanor was quickly smashed.

"Preacha, you'se gots ta help me!" the voice said softly.

"Dink, is that you?" I demanded, as I shot straight up in my bed, though I immediately regretted it due to the pain.

"Preacha, you'se gots ta help me!"

"Dink, where are you? How can I help you?"

He sounded like he was drugged or barely alive!

"Preacha, has I ever let ya down in yer many times...."

His voice fell off and the phone went dead.

I tried to sort out my mixed emotions. I wanted to believe that it was Dink and that he was still alive. But I also had to admit it might be more antics of Todd's over-all revenge scheme. But how would I ever know? Surely that was part of his plan---to play with me and with my emotions like a yo-yo. How cruel and heartless!

I have never felt so helpless in all my life! Here I was laid up in bed unable to help my best friend---if he was still alive. But what could I do even if I was healthy and able to go? Where would I go? What could I do?

If I could have gotten hold of Todd Shelton at this moment, I would have thrashed the living daylights out of him---right or wrong---even if Dink was still alive! But then I was reminded that vengeance belongs to the Lord (Romans 12:19). Another tension of Scripture, I thought!

I then found myself praying for Todd or whoever it was who was holding Dink---praying with tears streaming down my checks---both for Dink and for Todd!

What Can I Do?

I don't know how long I slouched in my bed praying and crying, feeling so helpless, yet realizing that was the condition God wanted me to be in so I could best pray for this whole situation.

I was drying my tears and sipping a cup of water, when Terry and my son, Ira, Jr., and my daughter, Beth, pushed the door open and came in. Ira, Jr. was 13 years old by now. He was very spiritually minded (still),[1] and a fine looking young man, taking after his mother in that department. And he was an aspiring young athlete, giving evidence of better skills in that area than I had possessed, though I had done fairly well in sports, when younger.

Beth was all of 10 years old now. She was as cute as a button, as the old saying goes, and if you will allow her father to say so. She was very friendly and quite innocent in so many areas. But she was the apple of her Daddy's eye!

Beth in her sweet innocent manner asked, "Daddy, are you sick?"

I smiled and explained that I had been hurt, but was getting better.

Ira, Jr. then wanted to know what had happened. Terry had not explained anything to the children. How could I tell them what was going on in just a few seconds? It was all so complicated.

Instead, not wanting them to worry, I merely said, "There was an accident, and I am not sure what caused it. But praise the Lord, I'm still here!"

Ira, Jr.'s next question was not so easy to answer.

"Wasn't Dink with you, Daddy? Is he all right?"

Terry saved me from having to answer that question, when she said, "Now, let Daddy rest. Wherever Dink is, he's in the Lord's hands too---just like Daddy was!"

Ira, Jr. asked just one more question---and what a question it was!

"Daddy, what were you doing at our school yesterday?"

"What?" I asked, not believing my ears had heard him correctly.

"What were you doing at school yesterday? I saw you at our school yesterday. What were you doing there?"

"You must be mistaken, son. I wasn't at your school yesterday!" I replied, trying to talk him out of his conviction.

"Yes, you were, Daddy! I would know you anywhere. You even waved to me and smiled!"

From further questioning I found out that I could not shake his belief that the man he had seen was me. My only conclusion could be that whoever was impersonating me, maybe even Todd, was at his school yesterday! I know I had not been there! What a frightful thought that was!!!

"Who was with me?" I asked, feeling stupid having to ask such a thing.

He smiled and replied, "Daddy, are you sure you aren't suffering from amnesia or something like that? You must have gotten a bump on your head in that accident, if you don't remember being at school yesterday!"

I let it go, but I had added another piece to the puzzle. Todd was or had been in town, as a previous report had said. What he was doing at the children's school, I do not know, unless it was to send me another message of fear and terror---that he had access to my children.

After about an hour of visiting, the family left, with instructions for the children to go to stay with Terry's parents, and for Terry to stay with Dink's wife, Janie, until this all came to an end. Then, I must have dozed off, but was awakened, yet still rather groggy, when the door of my room swung open. I squinted to see who was standing in the door, but the light on the table next to me blinded me somewhat. Whoever it was had on a hat and sunglasses, but then pulled them both off, and there he stood before me smiling at me! To my surprise, it was me!!

My first thought was that I must be dreaming, so I shook myself to bring me out of my drowsiness. Then he spoke, and was gone.

He said, "Dink said to tell you hello. He's dying!"

The strangest part was that his voice sounded just like mine!!

I also heard him laugh as he left the room, and I immediately hit the call button for the nurse to come. I got up to chase him, but when I got to the door, he was out of sight. The nurse scolded me for getting out of bed, and when I told her I had just seen a man that looked like me walk into the room, and then leave, she said, "You must have taken a stronger blow to the head than we thought!"

When I tried to explain the visitor and his visit further, the need to call the police, she just laughed, as if to humor one not quite right in the head, and after asking if I needed anything else, she left the room. As I reviewed what had just happened, did I dare call the police myself? And then came the question, what did my visitor mean by the comment, "Dink said to tell you hello, and he's dying!"

I could only shake my head at my dilemma. Here I am stuck in the hospital, and no one will believe me when I tell them there is a guy in town running around who looks like me! I have seen him and my son has seen him, but who would believe us? They would see my story as the result of a blow I took in the head yesterday in an explosion, and my son's as the wild tale of a youthful boy!

What was I going to do as puzzled as I was. I have to do something. But again, what could I do?

I looked at the clock, and it was 4:00 in the afternoon. I was afraid it was going to be another long evening and night!

---

[1]See the eighth book in this "journey" series by Richard P. Belcher. titled, *A Journey in Salvation*, (Columbia, SC: Richbarry Press), 2001.

12

Should I Stay in the Hospital?

After resting awhile, I knew I had to do something to pass the time---it was dragging so slowly. I needed to clear my name by proving I had not written the book on Roman Catholicism, for the sake of my job. But more seriously I needed to find Dink, if he was still alive, for his sake. But also I needed to find the joker who looked and talked like me (probably Todd), who had visited me in my hospital room and my son at school. I thought about leaving the hospital that evening, but decided against that idea when I got up to eat supper, and my head was still swimming. I had better get one more night's rest, and see what it's like in the morning. But what if I can't navigate in the morning?

Suddenly, unexpectedly there were two policemen in my room, wanting to ask me questions. I wondered if they had come on their own to follow-up their previous report, or had the nurse called for them, just to have them further check me out! I didn't have to wait long into the visit to find out they had been called by the nurse.

"We understand from the nurse that you thought you saw a man in your room that looked like you!" they began.

In a few words I tried to tell them my story, that is, all the events which had led up to the explosion in the house. How someone had tried to frame me, and then probably had set up the explosion. But the only thing they seemed interested in was if I really thought this man looked like me.

"Don't you think you could have been mistaken? Could you have been having hallucinations? Have you ever seen these kind of things before in your life? Are you presently seeing a psychologist? Do you need to see a psychologist?" And on and on they went, till it became apparent that they thought I had a major problem.

I heard them say to the nurse out in the hall as they left, "Keep a close eye on him! He really sounds confused!"

To which the nurse replied, "When I told the doctor about these hallucinations, he said we would look deeper into that tomorrow! Just give him another night to rest."

I agreed I would take another night to rest! But then early tomorrow, I was going to leave the hospital without their knowing it, before they tried to do something to me I would not allow, and which, even worse, would not allow me to try to do something to help Dink! I was sure they would conclude there was something seriously wrong with me, when I sneaked out of the hospital.

Then I realized I would face another major problem, if I left the hospital. Where would I go? The first place they would look would be at my house! I decided I needed to call Terry and tell her of my plans. She was at Janie's house, and glad to hear from me, but obviously she did not understand at first what I was going to do and why.

"You're leaving the hospital in the morning without telling them? Why would you do that?" she queried.

"Well, the man that Ira, Jr. saw yesterday, who looks like me, was in my room today!" I said softly.

I was glad now that Ira, Jr. had seen the man too. It didn't make me look like I had lost it.

"Yes, he was here, and he did look and talk just like me. I couldn't believe it. Trust me! I will call you, but we will use our favorite portion of the Bible as our password. You'll know from my quote that it's me."

After a few more instructions to Terry, I settled back into my bed to finish my plans for leaving the hospital. Then I thought to myself how idiotic this all sounds. I can't go home. So I have no place to go! No way to get there! Maybe I'm still not able to go because of my dizzy condition! I have no idea how to find the strange visitor, whoever he is, whenever I get to wherever I am going by whatever means I am getting there! I have no idea who might then be looking for me---the police? Or the strange visitor? I must admit that the bed felt very comfortable in light of the discomfort my thoughts were bringing. But I had to do something to find Dink---if he was still alive! Time could be very short!

And then a plan hit me! I would play the stranger's game. I would disguise myself! I would call Mac Turnover tonight! I would have him send someone to Seminary City and rent a car for me---one with dark windows so no one could see the driver! I would spend the days driving around the city looking for an appearance of the stranger. He had been out and about at least for awhile the past two days. Maybe I could catch him and follow him to wherever he was staying---maybe the place where he was keeping Dink!

Slim chance, one says? Then I reminded myself! Chance does not rule this world---His perfect providence does!!

13

Why Is the Bible Alone My Authority?

Before I went to bed, I decided to call Mac. I gave him all the details of the day, and my plans for the next morning. He suggested that I wait one more day, which would give me more strength, and then leave the hospital very early the next morning. He would send his man to Seminary City tomorrow, have him rent a car in his own name, and he would be waiting for me at 3:00 AM when I came out of the hospital. He would also rent a motel room, where I could sleep at night, while he drove through the city looking for someone who looked like me. Then he would sleep in the daytime, while I circled the city doing the same during the day. Or if I would rather drive at night in the dark in a car with shaded windows, I could do that also. Just reverse the order of driving and sleeping.

I must say my body and mind were relieved, when I stretched out on the bed again. I had a night and day to rest, and then another partial night, before having to make my break. I just hoped the hospital didn't get any strange ideas about my behavior and supposed hallucinations. I decided if they asked me anything about seeing myself in the room, I would make a joke out of it. Maybe then they would think I was back to normal---their view of normal.

After I called and informed Terry of the changed plans, I was further delighted that I could now turn to my study and add a few more thoughts to my notes before retiring for the night. But first, I wanted to summarize the main conclusions I had made concerning the subject.

1. There is a great distinction between the apostolic church of the New Testament period and the Roman Catholic Church at the time of the Reformation, and even a greater difference between the two at the latter part of the twentieth century.

2. The reason for the great difference between the two is that each one has a different authority structure.

   The Roman Catholic Church has a multi-source authority structure, which allows the church to change as the various areas of authority, including the church's history, tradition and other factors, interact with the Bible.

   The Reformers demanded that the church return to the doctrine of Sola Scriptura---Scripture alone---as the basis of authority. That means the church must be constantly testing itself in the area of its structure, practices and doctrine against Scripture to be sure it is what the New Testament said the church should be.

3. We had also concluded that the Roman Catholic Church had overbalanced toward the authority of the church in the matter of the tension, which must be held between the authority of the church, on one hand, and the Lordship of Christ over the individual believer's life, on the other hand. The overbalance towards the first had allowed the Roman Catholic Church to violate and deny the second, that is, the Lordship of Christ and the priesthood of the believer, which must be upheld in every Christian's life.

The question I had to face now was whether or not the New Testament taught the doctrine of Sola Scriptura---Scripture alone as our authority. It is well and good to talk of that doctrine, but does Scripture really teach it? And furthermore, does the Scripture teach the doctrines of the Lordship of Christ over the New Testament believer's life and the individual priesthood of every believer as well? We had already seen that the Scripture does teach the responsibility that a believer has to be submissive to the leaders of his church. But is that the only doctrine the New Testament teaches? Or does it also teach the other side of the tension---the necessity of the Lordship of Christ over my life, and the fact that I am a priest before God without any need of a representative for me before God except the Lord Jesus Christ?

I concluded that I would center my study on the doctrine of Sola Scripture on II Timothy 3:16-4:4:

3:16 All scripture is given by inspiration of God, and is profitable for doctrine, for reproof, for correction, for instruction in righteousness: 3:17 That the man of God may be perfect, throughly furnished unto all good works. 4:1 I charge thee therefore before God, and the Lord Jesus Christ, who shall judge the quick and the dead at his appearing and his kingdom; 4:2 Preach the word; be instant in season, out of season; reprove, rebuke, exhort with all longsuffering and doctrine. 4:3 For the time will come when they will not endure sound doctrine; but after their own lusts shall they heap to themselves teachers, having itching ears; 4:4 And they shall turn away their ears from the truth, and shall be turned unto fables.

I THE DOCTRINE OF SOLA SCRIPTURA RESTS SOLIDLY ON THE DOCTRINE OF THE DIVINE INSPIRATION OF SCRIPTURE

The text states
All Scripture is given by the inspiration of God...

A. Inspiration includes all the sacred Scripture

All Scripture is inspired of God. Thus, all 66 books of the Bible are inspired in their original manuscripts. Thus, we have a solid foundation for study and ministry.

B. Inspiration speaks of Scripture as being God-breathed---that is inspired by God

The word in the original language is *theopneusteo* ---Scripture was breathed out by God to the original writers, who recorded it in writing under divine inspiration. The result was that not just the writers were *inspired,* but the very writings bore the nature of divine inspiration. Thus, Scripture in its original language was God-breathed even to the words themselves.

Jesus said:

> *Man shall not live by bread alone, but by every word which proceeds from the mouth of God.*
> *Matthew 4:4*

> *For verily I say unto you, Till heaven and earth shall pass, one jot or tittle shall in no wise pass from the law till all be fulfilled.* (the word for "no wise" is a double negative---which is a very emphatic negative).
>
> *Matthew 5:18*

C. Divine inspiration must be carefully understood and defined lest we be guilty of robbing Scripture of its authority

1. <u>It is not that the writers alone were inspired</u>

There is a view known as neo-orthodoxy, which says that the writers had revelational encounters or experiences with God, and these experiences were inspired. But when men sought to write about these encounters, it must be remembered that one cannot put revelational truth on paper. Therefore, what they wrote was only their limited human witness of that glorious inspired encounter with God. But this leaves the Bible as a book of errors.

This is not the Biblical doctrine of inspiration. It is not that the writers were inspired, but what they wrote was a book of errors. The Bible teaches that inspiration extends to the very words of Scripture, and that the Bible writers wrote without error, even to the very words they used. Thus, it is not that the writers alone were inspired and their writings were not, but it is that inspiration extends to the very words which they wrote---even to the very jot or tittle of the words---that is, to the parts of the letters as well as the words.

2. <u>It is not that the ideas of the writers were inspired but the words were not</u>

    This is the belief that God gave the writers inspired thoughts, but they were left to choose the words with the result that Scripture must contain some error because of the human choices. If this was true, human choice would have to make further choices as to which words were true and which were not, or how close a word came to the truth or vice versa. Perhaps, part of the thought of a word was true, but not all. If that is the case, which part is true and which is not? One can surely see the chaos this would bring as one tried to study the Bible!

3. <u>It is not that the doctrinal parts of the Bible are inspired and perfect but the other parts are not</u>

    Some say when the Bible speaks of doctrine, we can trust it, but when the Bible speaks of other areas, such as geography, scientific matters, names of men, the exact history of an event, etc., we must question it! Not so! The text says that all Scripture is inspired of God.

4. <u>Summary</u>

It is not that only the men were inspired, but their writings were not! It is not that the men's ideas were inspired, but their words were not! It is not that the doctrine of the Bible was inspired, but the whole is not! It is that all Scripture and all parts of Scripture are inspired (God-breathed) even down to the very words and letters.

I like to put it this way. God in His full power used man in his full powers to write the Bible, and God so superintended the work that what the men wrote was inerrant and infallible, even to the very words they wrote, including all subjects they covered!

Or we can put it this way? God has revealed Himself in history and that revelation has been recorded in fullness in words in an inspired, inerrant, infallible Bible in its original manuscripts.

THEREFORE, WE HOLD FIRMLY TO THE DOCTRINE OF SOLA SCRIPTURA, BECAUSE THAT DOCTRINE RESTS ON THE DOCTRINE OF THE DIVINE INSPIRATION OF THE BIBLE.

This was the issue of the Reformation, as the Roman Catholic Church of that day had added many authorities to the authority of the Bible---authorities that were not divinely inspired and infallible. These fallible authorities included the traditions of the church, the writings of the church fathers, the decrees of the church councils, the decrees of the Pope, etc.

Thus, the question that must be faced is this: where does one find the statement that these other areas are inspired of God? That is, where is the authoritative statement (1) that the traditions of the church are divinely inspired? (2) that any of the writings of the church fathers are divinely inspired? (3) that any decrees of the church are divinely inspired? (4) that any sayings or writings or decrees of the popes are divinely inspired?

I wasn't finished with this section of discussion, but I decided I had better go to bed early this night to prepare for the coming days. As I laid back in the bed just resting for a few moments, I was suddenly aware of someone in the room with me. And there he was---the man who looked exactly like me. He was standing about five feet from the bed, just smiling. Finally, he spoke.

"Dink said to tell you hello, and that he wanted you to hurry up and find him! He might not be alive very long!"

With a smirk and a devilish laugh, he turned and bolted out the door. I also finally punched the call button for the nurse, which I had been seeking inconspicuously while Mr. Imitator was in the room. As I waited for a response (it took a couple of minutes---no hurry on their part), I recalled I had a problem. I asked myself, what I would tell them---that the man who looked like me was back? Not on your life!! I just asked the nurse for a drink of water!!

14

What Shall I Do Now?

As I sipped my unneeded water, I had some second thoughts about leaving the hospital. As long as I was in this hospital room, the strange visitor might keep on trying to torment me. Wouldn't it be better to try to set a trap for him? But then, how many more times was he going to try to slip in and out of the hospital (whatever route he was taking), without getting caught? Maybe I would be better off waiting outside the hospital, keeping watch to see if I could catch him going in or out again?

Supposing he wouldn't return again that night, I finally fell asleep, hoping the spells of dizziness and headaches would be gone when I awoke the next day. But it was not my privilege to sleep through the night, as I awoke to someone shaking me. It was the nurse, and she was addressing me with a loud and strong voice.

"Mr. Pointer, wake up! You must wake up! You've been talking about seeing that man again---that one that you think looks and talks like you! Wake up! Wake up!"

She finally shook me to my senses, and I was like a man awaking from a Sunday afternoon nap---groggy and wondering what day it was and where I was. When she was finally certain that I was fully awake, she took off for somewhere like a bolt of lightening. I was left to guess where she had gone and when she would be back. I looked at my watch and it was about midnight.

I had no idea what I had said or done while asleep, nor what she might due in response to my actions. Would they drug me to help control me? Would I be secured somewhere behind bars to keep me from any further such reactions, or even more serious upheavals? Would I, or my wife, Terry, have any recourse, if they put me away somewhere in an asylum? More seriously, how long would they keep me there, which was an especially important question in light of the premium on time for the next few days---especially if Dink really was alive and seriously ill, as the imposter had indicated?

I made a quick decision! I must leave the hospital immediately---right now! Quickly, I threw on my clothes, grabbed my personal items, along with my study notes, peered into the hospital corridor, and seeing it empty, I was gone. I stumbled, because of some dizziness, down the back stairway (from the fifth floor), and opened the door on the first floor to see if the coast was clear. It was, so out into the night I went.

I had to admit that the cooler night air seemed to refresh me, as I made my way through the parking lot, trying to appear like any normal hospital visitor. If the imposter had made it safely through the night, why couldn't I? But where would I go? Then I remembered that I still had a key to my office at school. Maybe I could slip in past the night watchman, and sleep on the couch for the rest of the night, at least, and leave before dawn the next day.

But what if the hospital called the police, when they found me missing? Maybe they would even consider me dangerous, because they thought I was having some kind of hallucinations. Wouldn't my office at school be one of the first places they would check? I decided I had no choice! There was no where else to go!

After walking in the shadows of trees, and hiding behind parked cars, and taking to the bushes when a car approached, I made my way down the side streets, and finally came to the seminary. My head was throbbing by now, and I was also dizzy (I had probably traveled two miles or more), and my heart was pounding. The seminary campus was quiet as I sneaked again from tree to tree to the building which housed my office.

Noting that the watchman was nowhere to be seen, I opened the door of Merrimount Hall, made my way down to my office, and silently but carefully unlocked it, pushed it open, then secured it tightly behind me, and collapsed on the couch. I was breathing deeply and my heart and head were pounding, as if they were going to burst open any moment, no doubt, because of my physical condition and the harrowing strain on my frail nerves.

I felt fairly safe, but safe or not, my exhausted body craved sleep. I had to get some sleep. I couldn't afford to stay awake and watch for someone looking for me. I was in the Lord's hands! I thought of several verses of Scripture, as I dozed off to sleep.

I laid me down and slept; I awaked; for the LORD sustained me. Psalm 3:5

I will both lay me down in peace, and sleep: for thou, LORD, only makest me dwell in safety. Psalm 4:8

...he giveth his beloved sleep. Psalm 127:2

When thou liest down, thou shalt not be afraid: yea, thou shalt lie down, and thy sleep shall be sweet.
Proverbs 3:24

15

Did I Really Find You Here?

I tossed and turned on the couch through the night, fearful that I would oversleep the next morning. As I stirred about 4:30 AM, I tried to figure out when I needed to get up, and where I was going to go when I did rise. Then I remembered that today was Saturday. I was in a secured building, so not even students would be stirring in my area. There might be the possibility that some faculty members, who had offices in the building, would come in to do some work, but that would be no problem. No one else had a key to my office (that I knew of), and since there would be no reason for any one to get into the office, why couldn't I just hide there for the day, even from the police.

I also remembered that I had some crackers and cheese type snacks, along with some cokes or something in my small icebox, so why not stay there? I didn't even need to use any light, in case I wanted to pursue my current study on the Roman Catholic Church, and I had no window on my door, so no one in the hall could see into the room. The windows were on the backside of the building, which was a parking lot for the maintenance workers. Most of them did not work on Saturdays. Thus, I could leave the blinds open, and no one would see me.

I cannot tell you how good it felt, to not have to get up at 4:30 AM (especially in light of my still light and dizzy head), and try to sneak around the city, to say nothing of the difficulty of trying to find another hiding place for the day. I surely could not go home, as that was the first place they would look for me. But before I went back to sleep for a few more hours, I decided I needed a plan to hide, just in case the police came looking for me.

I remembered again (nothing wrong with my memory now) that my door had a unique lock, which enabled me to press in the middle of the doorknob on the inside. Then anyone putting a key into the middle of the doorknob from the outside (the normal way to unlock it and open the door), would not be able to work his key, unless he jostled it just right, which usually took a number of seconds. That would give me enough time to climb out the back window into the bushes, and close the window behind me, before the intruder came in and caught me.

I arranged things so it would not look like I had been there, and then I went back to sleep, and slept lightly as before, and to my joy, nothing disturbed me for the next three hours, when I finally decided to get up. After eating some of my snacks, and drinking a coke, and again cleaning up any evidence that I had been there, I rested once again. I began trying to figure out how I was going to get in contact with Mac's man, when he was expecting to see me at the hospital at 3:00 AM tomorrow morning.

Then I remembered that I had my little transistor radio on my desk, and I probably should see what the local news was saying, if anything, about my escape from the hospital. I smiled as I thought of the possibility of the police warning the community about my being loose! As I tuned in, it sounded like the most exciting event of the history of Seminary City! The announcers were interviewing everybody and his brother, asking in their most serious voices, if anyone had seen anything of this madman who was on the loose. I listened to a number of them telling the audience, "And now we take you to so and so over at such and such a place to get the latest on this developing story." You would have thought they were covering the assassination of a president or something serious.

First, they talked to some doctors, some I don't think I had ever seen. Then, they talked to my evening nurse, who described my supposed bizarre behavior. Then, they talked to some psychologists, who gave their interpretation of what could have caused me to have such hallucinations. One suggested that it was clear that I surely was mentally confused previously. I was a man who was teaching at a Baptist seminary, but then I also had written a book saying why I was going to become something else.

Some experts tried to predict what I might be expected to do next. The answers ran all the way from one extreme to the other---I was harmless, or I was extremely dangerous. Next, they went to a police spokesman, and asked him where he thought the police might find me. He informed the audience that there weren't very many places I could go. He gave the expected answers---his house, his friends, and his office. Then, he said someone was on the way to check out my office at the Seminary---probably not usual police procedure---to give such details. I wondered why they had not come here in the first place.

I smiled as I said, "Thank you, sir!" and then made my way to the window and crawled out to hide in the bushes. I did leave the window cracked, very slightly, which shouldn't raise any suspicion. I wanted to hear any conversation inside the room. Within five minutes they were there, three or four of them, and after they had figured out how to open my door, they scoured my room for any evidence that I had been there. One officer raised the window and looked out, but I was well screened from his view by the shrubbery.

Then I heard one of them say, "Well, he's not here now, and he doesn't appear to have been here last night. Let's check the outside of the building."

When I heard the door shut in my office, and was certain that they were gone, I crawled back through the window, closing it to the same place it had been previously, in case they checked the window from the outside. I then hid in the closet, knowing someone would look through the window from the outside. I heard their muffled voices for awhile through the closet door, and then they were gone. I left my closet hideaway, and sought the couch to rest with a smile on my face and praise in my heart. It seemed that the Lord was watching over me! In His providence He had given me clear warning they were coming! Now, all I had to do was occupy the time till I went to meet Mac's man at 3:00 AM at the hospital.

But, all of a sudden, as I was resting joyfully in my triumph, a key was rattling in the door of the office once again. I didn't have time to get out the window, so I took refuge in my closet hideaway. Through the crack in the closet door, I saw the outside door of the office opening. My heart pounded! Had I come through all of this to go back to who-knows-where to be secured in who-knows-what to be examined by who-knows-who?

And then my heart lifted as I saw it was Terry!! But I didn't reveal myself quickly, because I didn't know who was with her. She closed the door behind her, and I knew she was alone. Softly I said, "Terry!" She jumped, and then I stepped out from the closet. For a few minutes we just stood there and hugged each other and cried. She seemed as spent as I was!

What Are the Results of Sola Scriptura?

Terry shared with me that she knew why I had left the hospital. They had explained the circumstances, but she didn't bother to try to tell them anything different from their interpretation. They had their minds made up! She had given the whole situation over to the Lord.

She informed me that she too had heard on the radio that the police were going to my office, and that is when she decided she would come here also. When she saw them leaving, she told them who she was, and that there were some things in my office that she wanted to get. They were very friendly and helpful, she said, and didn't seem to suspect anything.

Before she left, and I did understand that she could not stay too long, she told me she had been in touch with Mac by a pay phone. He said his man would pick me up one block away from the seminary at the corner of Docket and Marshall Streets. She noted that it was one of the most convenient places for me to reach from the seminary, and also one of the darkest and most deserted streets in town. Then she pulled out some things she thought I might need (including some food), we embraced again, prayed together, and with further tears she departed.

By now it was getting close to ten o'clock in the morning, and after some nourishment from the food Terry had brought, I slept a few more hours, not deeply, but comfortably with great enjoyment. I left my little radio on only loud enough for my ear to hear it, as it was positioned under the couch pillow, in case something useful to me was said. Then I decided it was time to stretch my brain on my study of theology!

The first thing I did was to review my previous study, since this one would be a continuation of it. I had begun a study of II Timothy 3:16-17 through 4:4. I noted the main thoughts once again.

I THE DOCTRINE OF SOLA SCRIPTURA RESTS SOLIDLY ON THE DOCTRINE OF THE DIVINE INSPIRATION OF SCRIPTURE

The text states
All Scripture is given by inspiration of God

A. Inspiration includes all sacred Scripture

B. Inspiration speaks of Scripture as being God-breathed---that is inspired by God

C. Divine inspiration must be carefully understood and defined lest we be guilty of robbing Scripture of its authority

1. It is not that the writers alone were inspired

2. It is not that the ideas of the writers were inspired but not their words

3. It is not that the doctrinal parts of the Bible are inspired and perfect, but the other parts are not

4. <u>It is that the very writings themselves are inspired---even to the very words</u>

THEREFORE, WE FIRMLY HOLD TO THE DOCTRINE OF SOLA SCRIPTURA-------, BECAUSE THE DOCTRINE OF SOLA SCRIPTURA RESTS FIRMLY ON THE DOCTRINE OF THE DIVINE INSPIRATION OF THE BIBLE.

This was the issue of the Reformation, as the Roman Catholic Church of that day had added many authorities to the authority of the Bible, authorities that were not divinely inspired and infallible. These fallible authorities included the traditions of the church, the writings of the church fathers, the decrees of the church councils, and the authority of papal decrees, etc.

Thus, the question that has to be faced is this: where does one find the statement that these other areas are inspired of God? That is, where is the authoritative statement from God that the traditions of the church are divinely inspired? That any of the writings of the church fathers are divinely inspired? That any decrees of the church are divinely inspired? That any sayings or writings or decisions of the popes are divinely inspired?

Then I began to deal with my second main point of the study.

II THE DOCTRINE OF SOLA SCRIPTURA RESULTS IN THE POWER OF SCRIPTURE TO PREPARE THE INDIVIDUAL BELIEVER FOR EVERY GOOD WORK

Our text says that because all Scripture is inspired of God, it is profitable therefore for doctrine, for reproof, for correction, for instruction in righteousness, so that the man of God may be perfectly and completely prepared for every good work

Thus, the profitability of Scripture for the individual believer in his personal life in the stated above areas is based on the inspiration and infallibility of the Bible, but the profitability here speaks not of a profitability for preaching to others, though that is certainly true. Rather, it speaks of the profitability of Scripture for the individual Christian to be completely prepared for any and every good work that God might call him to do. That is to say, that the individual Christian must be using and interacting with the Bible daily, so that he will be profited in the various areas, so that he will be ready for his ministry.

Notice that this speaks of the individual Christian and his interaction with the Bible and its profitability for him. There is no mention here of the church's authority or the church's interpretation of the Scripture to him.

A. The doctrine of Sola Scriptura prepares the believer for every good work, and because the Bible is inspired and infallible, it is profitable for doctrine.

Whether we realize it or not, every one has a doctrinal system of beliefs---the Christian and the non-Christian. It may be a very simple one. Or it may be a very complex one. It may be a true and accurate one, or it may be a false and dangerous one. It may be a combination of truth and error. But the point is that everyone has a doctrinal system. The Christian must be careful to build his doctrinal system on the Bible---not on the beliefs of the church, or on the church's interpretation of the Bible, or on some famous scholar of the past or present. It is the individual Christian who is building his doctrinal system, and he must be careful to build that system on the Bible.

B. The doctrine of Sola Scriptura prepares the believer for every good work because the Bible is inspired and infallible and is profitable for reproof.

This again does not speak of my using the inspired Bible to correct others to whom I speak and minister, but this speaks of my using the Bible to reprove any false understanding I may have in my doctrinal system, as it develops.

C. The doctrine of Sola Scriptura prepares the believer for every good work because the Bible is inspired and infallible and therefore profitable for correction.

I am to use the Bible, not only to reprove any error in my doctrinal system, but I am to use it also to correct my doctrinal system, where it has been shown to be in error by the Bible.

D. **The doctrine of Sola Scriptura prepares the believer for every good work because the Bible is inspired and infallible, and therefore, it is profitable for instruction in righteousness.**

The Bible not only teaches us doctrine, telling us who God is, and who man is, and what sin is, and who Christ is, and how I can be saved, etc., but it also teaches me how to live a holy life! It instructs me in righteous living, holiness of life, godliness in my walk, prayer, the keeping of my heart before God, mortifying and dealing with sin, godly repentance, how to live the Christian life, etc.

E. **Now all of the above speaks of the individual believer studying and applying the Scripture for himself, whereby Scripture then prepares him completely to do any good work that God would call him to do.**

Thus, the Bible is profitable to the individual believer's life in all of these areas because it is divinely inspired of God. If the Bible is not inspired, it cannot be profitable in any of these areas. And I say again that this speaks of my responsibility before God to study the Bible to find the truth, not of the church's mandating beliefs to me.

III SOLA SCRIPTURA REACHES BEYOND THE INDIVIDUAL WITH THE COMMAND FROM PAUL TO PREACH THE WORD TO OTHERS IN AN AUTHORITATIVE MANNER

1 I charge thee therefore before God, and the Lord Jesus Christ, who shall judge the quick and the dead at his appearing and his kingdom; 2 Preach the word; be instant in season, out of season; reprove, rebuke, exhort with all longsuffering and doctrine. 3 For the time will come when they will not endure sound doctrine; but after their own lusts shall they heap to themselves teachers, having itching ears; 4 And they shall turn away their ears from the truth, and shall be turned unto fables. II Timothy 4:1-4

A. Because of Sola Scriptura we have here a command to preach the Bible to others.

Remember that the previous passage (II Timothy 3:16-17), which we have been dealing with, does not speak of preaching the Word of God to others. But II Timothy 4:1-4 does speak of preaching to others. The preparation for every good work includes the preparation to preach and teach the Word to others.

We are to preach the Word! Not the tradition of the church! Not the writings of the church fathers! Not the decisions of the church councils! Not the decrees of a pope! But preach the Word of God--- that is a command! Preach the divinely inspired, infallible, inerrant Word of God.   That is our authority!

B. Because of Sola Scriptura we have a command to preach the Word at all times and in every situation---the Bible is our authority in every case.

Be instant in season and out of season

when it brings rejoicing or when it offends!
when it brings repentance or when it brings scorn!
when it brings praise or when it brings rejection!
when it causes men to love us or hate us!
when it draws a crowd or scatters a crowd!
when men hear it or when they do not hear it!
when it brings reward or when it costs you dearly!
when men respond and when men do not respond!

preach the word

in every situation
in every season
in every circumstance
at every opportunity

C. Because of Sola Scriptura we are to preach the Word for it will reprove, rebuke, and exhort with all long suffering and doctrine.

1. We are to preach the Word because it brings conviction of sin

It will not always make people feel good, giving fuzzy feelings and warm emotions! It will rather reprove and convict of sin! It will lay sin bare to our understanding! It will expose sin and spiritual nakedness before God!

2. <u>We are to preach the Word because it will rebuke men of their sin</u>

The Scripture will not only lay sin bare, but it will rebuke sin and challenge a man's attitude and lifestyle of sin! It will even challenge a man's denial or his justification of sin or a tendency to ignore sin!

3. <u>We are to preach the Word with exhortation</u>

Preaching the Bible will exhort men to leave their sin, to repent of their sin, to place their faith in Christ, to cast themselves on Christ alone as Savior, to live a godly and righteous life, to love God and His Word, and to hate sin!

4. <u>We are to preach the Word with love and truth</u>

Some preachers are syrupy and mushy-sweet with love, while others are strong in doctrine but without love or kindness! We must have both, for either one without the other is lopsided and is harmful to the gospel! We must have longsuffering and doctrine and a love for the truth.

5.   We must realize that not all men will receive the preaching of the Word

The text says that the time will come when men will not love sound doctrine. Thus, not all men will love the truth; not all men will want the truth; not all men will recognize sound doctrine! Some men will embrace false doctrine! The time will come when men will heap to themselves certain kinds of teachers, because they have itching ears! Men will not want nor like strong preaching, that is, preaching which reproves, rebukes and exhorts them from Scripture! Men will want to hear that which entertains; that which merely excites and stirs the emotions; that which is only sensational; that which satisfies the sinful nature of man; that which does not upset them or convict them of sin; that which is shallow and fluffy with no strong doctrine!

Thus, it is the infallible Word of God, because it has become profitable to us, which also becomes profitable through us, as we preach it to others!

This is Sola Scriptura---Scripture alone! And because it is the Word of God, it can do the work of God.

The Scripture mentions no other person, or group of persons, or organization, or even any other documents, which are equal to the Bible or higher than the Bible in its certainty, centrality, power and authority---all because it is the divinely inspired Word of God. That is

Sola Scriptura! Where are such statements concerning any other authority for His church or for the individual?

Oh, that we would beware of any church or denomination, which does not hold to the doctrine of Sola Scriptura!

As I finished these notes, I noticed it was early afternoon and time for me to rest once more. As I gave my attention to the news, I noticed they were still giving the mystery of my disappearance and my danger to the community top billing. If they only knew the truth and where I was really hiding!

But for now I must rest. Who knew what my evening meeting with Mac's man might bring? Would he be there? Would I be able to stay here till it was time to meet him? It was all in God's hands---no better place to be!

17

Do I Finally Have a Clue?

I was so exhausted mentally and physically, that I fell off to sleep and didn't awaken until about 9:00 PM. I wanted to pursue my study further, but I didn't dare turn on any lights. So for the first few minutes or so, I sat in the dark and just relaxed and thought.

I had six hours before I was to meet the man Mac was sending. I would leave the seminary at about 2:45 AM, and that would give me plenty of time to get to the corner of Docket and Marshall. I hoped not, but I might need the extra time to dodge the night watchman or some unforeseen person or event between the seminary and the appointed place of meeting.

I must admit, I began to get antsy. Not only had I been here at the seminary too long, but precious time had passed, and I knew nothing further about the status of Dink. Was he still alive? Was he ever alive after the explosion? How badly hurt was he, if he was alive at all? And the most difficult question of all---how were we going to find him, if he was alive?

Then all of a sudden, I was aware of something in the dark room that I had not noticed since waking up. I was not the only one present in the room, so it seemed. I saw the silhouette of something standing over near the window, so motionless and silent, that I wondered if someone had put a coat rack in my office in my absence. I had not seen one during the day, so I decided it must be a person. I also determined that I would not make any quick movement, but would lie motionless to wait and see what his next move would be. It had to be him---the man who looked like me! But how did he find out where I was hiding, and how had he gotten in the room without a key? And why hadn't he made some move previously, while I was sleeping?

Finally, he began to move slowly, and I continued to remain motionless, trying to determine his next move. Was he coming towards me or was he heading quietly towards the door to leave, as he had entered? Then my heart was filled with terror, as I saw something in his hand, as the outside light flashed on it. I rolled off the couch onto the floor, just as he raised a knife and brought it down on the spot I had just vacated. I tried to kick the knife out of his hand from my position on the floor, but though I gave him what must have been a painful blow with my shoe, he was still clinging to the knife. While he recovered from my kick, I sprang to my feet, and then saw him coming at me with greater fervor than before.

I don't know exactly how it happened. But as we struggled for the knife, I gripped his arm, and as I sought to wrench the knife from him, he gave one great burst of energy to get away from me. But instead of freeing himself from my grasp, he fell into the knife, and gave a ghastly shriek of pain as it cut into his body. I am not certain exactly where the knife entered his body, nor how far it penetrated, but he then fell hard to the floor. I knew it would be only seconds before he would react like a wounded animal, and come at me again with even a greater ferocity. Therefore, I decided that I had to press the battle further, for the sake of finding Dink. If I could only subdue him, perhaps I could force him to tell me all I longed to know about Dink and his physical status.

Thus, for the next few moments it seemed we were in a life and death struggle, and though I heard him gurgle and groan several times, he never evidenced any loss of strength. Finally, he broke loose from my grip, and headed for the door, and disappeared into the night. I wanted to follow him, but that was too risky, and I was too exhausted. I managed to crawl across the floor to lock the door behind him, although I wondered what good that would do, if he had gotten in before without a key. I fell to the floor again, gasping for breath.

My visitor had to be the mystery man. But how did he know where I was? What had he intended to do to me? If he had wanted to kill me, why did he wait till I was awake? And how did he get into my office? What would he do now, seeing he knew where I was? Would he call the police? Was he calling them just now? Could they be on their way to the campus this very moment?

Quickly, I decided I had to get out of here. Thus, again I gathered up my belongings. But in God's providence, as I swept the floor with my hand for something I might have lost in the struggle or something scattered in the fight, I brushed across a card or something. Knowing I couldn't turn on the lights, and that there was no time to look at it now, I put it securely in a pocket. As I climbed out the back window, I heard the sirens and saw the lights of police cars coming up the long driveway leading to the various buildings of the seminary. I made my way in the darkness across campus to the other side of campus.

I concluded that my night visitor had called the police. I wondered what he had told them concerning his encounter with me, if anything. I wondered also what they would soon conclude from seeing the crime scene with blood all over the floor.

18

Who Is Dr. Flowers?

As I made my escape through the dark, I wondered if I might find some placc to hide over near Docket and Marshall Streets, while I waited for my contact man to rescue me. By now it was past 9:30 PM, which meant that I had more than a five-hour wait for my ride. I wondered how I would ever dodge the police for that length of time, since they would have to conclude that I had just recently left my place of hiding at the seminary. Plus, my energy level was on low---maybe even empty, by now.

Whoever said the area of Docket and Marshall was a dark and desolate and deserted place, had made an understatement. It was so dark and desolate, I was frightened even to hang around the area, let alone hide in its innermost reaches. I had no idea what kind of unfriendly beings I might find in the shadows and pockets of the darkness, which engulfed the area. And I had no flashlight! It was such a scary mess that the traffic was non-existent--- even the police cars did not search this place for me. Surely, they must have concluded I would never go there to find another place of refuge, for only the most desperate man would hide there. A man would be better resting in jail than to try to hide in this abyss.

As I was hiding near the appointed corner, not daring to venture very deep into the brush, a car came down the street. Could it be a police car? It stopped at one extremity of the corner, and I heard a voice saying, "The Lord is my shepherd! I shall not want!"

Could it be my contact man? Slowly, I made my approach to the car and the driver from behind. He kept repeating quietly, but in the strongest whisper possible, the words of Psalm 23.

I think I shocked him, when out of the darkness I said, "Are you Mac's man?"

He seemed as relieved as I was, when he said, "Yes! Jump in and let's get out of here!"

He didn't have to tell me twice. I didn't even take time to go around the car to get in on the passenger side, but dove into the back seat, and said, "I agree, let's get out of here---now!" Not wanting to draw attention, he smoothly accelerated, and I gave a sigh of relief as I slouched in the back seat as we got into the normal flow of traffic. True, we had darkened windows, but I still didn't want to sit up, even though I knew no one could see me.

He introduced himself as Phil Scott. When I noted that he was early, he said he was cruising around town, waiting till it was time to pick me up, when he heard the sirens and saw the police cars going up towards the seminary buildings. Knowing I was hiding in the seminary, he figured they were looking for me. He figured if I had gotten away from them, I might be at our rendezvous early. So he came looking for me. And was I ever glad.

As we rode towards our motel, I pulled the card I had found on the floor of my office out of my pocket. In the dark it felt like a business card. I asked Phil if he had a small flashlight, and when he handed me one, I slouched even farther towards the floor while I read it. It was the card of a doctor---a plastic surgeon. If the intruder in my office was the same guy who had visited me previously, who looked like my twin, could this be the doctor who had given him my identity?

19

Why Is Sola Scriptura So Important?

When we got to the motel, Phil had arranged two rooms. When I asked him if that might not cause some suspicion, he answered that he had rented the rooms in the name of Turnover News Agency, Mack's company. He also told the manager of the motel that he was a reporter, and he and his companion would be working on the Ira Pointer story. Thus, he had told the truth---he was from the Turnover News Agency, and we would be working on the now all consuming story of Seminary City---the most intriguing story of several decades. I was glad to know that I was working with an honest man!

When I got into my room, my sleep patterns were so confused, that my body refused to cooperate with my desire to conk out. So at about eleven o'clock, after such a rugged day, I turned on the television, and again, I could not believe what I was hearing. The story being reported was that the police had received an anonymous phone call from one of my students, and I had lured him to my office early in the evening. The police had concluded that I must have entered the seminary building after they had searched the office, and after my wife had visited there. Though I was somewhat frustrated that the police were presenting the events to put themselves in the best light, I was glad to hear they were not going to lay any blame on Terry.

But, to continue the story, when my student arrived at the office, he refused to help me, and I attacked him with a knife! He was able to escape, but only after a bloody fight, which left him wounded. As for the reason he would not give his name, he said he did not want to get involved! Nonetheless, the police and the media outlets were believing the story on the testimony of a supposed student sight unseen, but they had to admit, that though I was in the room prior to their raid, I had once again eluded their best efforts to capture me.

The talking heads of the media were again very serious in their analysis of the story and supposed sub plots. The man who had been in such a severe explosion, and probably had lost his best friend, who had then suffered delusions and hallucinations, had now become violent in his demands on others to help him. All friends, students and former students, and others who had known me in any manner in the past, were advised to contact the police, immediately, if I contacted them. My picture (and not a very good one, at that) was splattered all over the television screen. The whole scenario would have been funny, if it were not so tragic.

Not being able to sleep, and being totally frustrated over the news stories, I decided to move a little further in my thoughts on the subject of Roman Catholicism.

I had shown the great importance of Sola Scripture. I had presented its definition and Biblical foundation. I had shown the Biblical tension between a Christian's being submissive to the leaders of his church versus his duty also to be faithful to the Lordship of Jesus Christ and the doctrine of the priesthood of every believer (one mediator between God and man). I had also contended that Sola Scriptura is the main difference between Catholics and Protestants. That is to say, the Roman Catholic system developed not from the Scriptures as its authority, but from all the other supposed authorities added to the Scriptures---councils, popes, traditions, etc.

Thus, at the time of the Reformation period, when men began to realize the need to return to the doctrine of Sola Scriptura, there was a major distinction between the Reformation beliefs based on a Biblical foundation and the Roman Catholic Church based on their multi-source foundation.

In order to illustrate that great distinction and the necessity of the doctrine of Sola Scriptura, I had decided to use one very major doctrine of the Roman Catholic Church---the doctrine of Mary. I knew this would be quite controversial, because so many Roman Catholics have been reared with and continue to possess such a strong veneration of Mary. Could I ever ask them to listen to my presentation of a comparison of Mary as found in the Scripture and the Mary now presented by the Roman Catholic Church? And would they even begin to consider the weak reasoning and evidence for the change in the doctrine of Mary, as it was based on the Roman Catholic authority structure and not Scripture? I could only pray that any Roman Catholic reading the final results of my labors would be open to listen to my arguments---agree or disagree.

What the Scriptures Say about Mary

It must be acknowledged by all, even Roman Catholics, that the Scriptural data concerning Mary is very slim. Note the following Scriptural references, and realize this is all the Bible says about her.

1. <u>Scripture says Christ was born of a virgin</u>

   a. Isaiah 7:14

      *Therefore the Lord himself shall give you a sign;
      Behold, a virgin shall conceive, and bear a son, and
      shall call his name Immanuel.*

   b. Matthew 1:23

      *Behold, a virgin shall be with child, and shall bring
      forth a son, and they shall call his name Emmanuel,
      which being interpreted is, God with us.*

   c. Luke 1:26-27

      *26 And in the sixth month the angel Gabriel was
      sent from God unto a city of Galilee, named
      Nazareth, 27 To a virgin espoused to a man whose
      name was Joseph, of the house of David; and the
      virgin's name was Mary.*

2. <u>Scripture says that Mary did not remain a perpetual
   virgin after she had born Christ</u>

   a. Matthew 1:24-25

      *24 Then Joseph being raised from sleep did as the
      angel of the Lord had bidden him, and took unto
      him his wife: 25 And knew her not <u>till</u> she had
      brought forth her firstborn son: and he called his
      name JESUS.* (emphasis mine)

When the text states that Joseph knew not his wife until[1] she had brought forth her firstborn son, the statement limits her virginity only until the time of the birth of the Messiah. After that, Joseph and Mary had a normal marital relationship. She was not, according to Scriptures, a perpetual virgin the rest of her life.

    b.   Matthew 12:47-50 (these passages are paralleled in Mark 3:31-35 and Luke 8:19-21)

47 Then one said unto him, Behold, thy mother and thy <u>brethren</u>[2] stand without, desiring to speak with thee. 48 But he answered and said unto him that told him, Who is my mother? and who are my <u>brethren</u>? 49 And he stretched forth his hand toward his disciples, and said, Behold my mother and my <u>brethren</u>! 50 For whosoever shall do the will of my Father which is in heaven, the same is my brother, and sister, and mother.

In this passage the text not only indicates that Christ had brothers born of Mary, but that He also possessed a higher family---those born of God spiritually. This is not to totally deny His human family, but it does show us He had brothers, and though He respected His mother and brothers, He did not give Mary the veneration that the Roman Catholic Church does today.

3. <u>Luke has several other truths to add to the person of Mary in Luke 1</u>

verse 26

Mary was visited by angel Gabriel as she lived in Nazareth.

verse 27

Mary was a virgin when the angel appeared, and she was espoused to Joseph (engaged---but a much stronger term than our word for engagement today).

verse 28

The angel told her she was highly favored among women, and that the Lord was with her, and she was blessed among women. Certainly, Mary was highly favored and blessed among women, in that she was chosen to bear Jesus Christ the Messiah. And without doubt, the Lord was with her.

verse 29

Understandably, also, is the fact that Mary was puzzled by this message from the angel. Who was she to bear the Messiah?

verse 30

Gabriel encourages her not to fear, but to understand that she has found favor with God.

verse 31

The angel then gives further information concerning her chosen role---she will conceive in her womb, and she shall bring forth a son, and she shall call His name Jesus.

verses 32-33

The focus of the angel's message now turns from Mary to her son. He shall be great and He shall be called the Son of the Highest, and He shall be given the throne of His father David. He shall reign over the house of Jacob forever, and His kingdom is to be one that shall never end. Clearly, He is the one who shall be exalted, not Mary, though she certainly is to be respected for her life and work.

verses 34-35

Mary then raises the proper question---How can these things be, in light of the fact she has not had any relationship with a man? The angel has the answer, and it is an amazing one. The Holy Spirit will come upon her, and the power of the Highest shall overshadow her, and therefore that holy one who shall be born of her shall be called the Son of God. Yes, Mary by the power of the Holy Spirit, and not by the power of human means, will be the mother of the incarnate Son of God.

verses 36-37

Mary is then told that Elizabeth, her cousin, has also conceived in her old age (though in a natural manner, even though she had been considered barren), because with God all things are possible. Thus we have noted here two unusual births---one was a virgin birth, while the other was a natural birth involving some extenuating circumstances. Mary is reminded that God is able to do all things.

verses 38-45

These verses record Mary's humble agreement with and submission to God's will for her life, and that she then paid a visit to Elizabeth, her cousin (the future mother of John the Baptist). When Elizabeth heard the message of Mary, Elizabeth's child now leaped in her womb, and Elizabeth was filled with the Holy Spirit. She spoke with a loud voice declaring again that Mary was blessed among women, and so was the fruit of her womb. She marveled that the mother of her Lord would come and visit her.

verses 46-55

Mary praised the Lord for regarding her low estate, noting that all generations to come would recognize that she had been blessed of God to be allowed to bear the Messiah. She continued to praise the Lord with glorious recognition of His person, might and mercy.

verse 56

Mary then stayed with Elizabeth three months, and after this time returned to her own home.

The point we would emphasize is that though Mary is highly favored and to be sincerely recognized as such, there is no mention of the many ideas which have evolved in the Roman Catholic Church about her, such as the following:

a. Her immaculate conception, which is the idea that Mary was free from original sin from the moment of her conception.

b. Her bodily assumption, which is the idea that she was preserved from the corruption of the tomb, and like her Son, she conquered death, and was raised body and soul to the glory of heaven.

c. Her work as a co-redeemer with Christ, which is the idea that she, through what she herself suffered in the death of her son, Jesus Christ, may justly be said to have redeemed with Christ the human race. (see the writings of Pope Benedict XV, 1914-1922, from his Apostolic Letter, *Inter Sodalacia*, 182, plus many other similar statements by the Roman Catholic Church and its leaders).

If one were to ask why and how such ideas could arise concerning Mary (and so many other subjects), the answer is clear. It is because the Roman Catholic Church through history was not tied to the doctrine of Sola Scripture, but rather it was left to free wheel concerning its doctrines, even to the point of contradicting the clear teachings of the Bible!

---

[1]This is the Greek adverb *heos* used as an improper preposition with the genitive of the relative pronoun *hos*. Used without the negative, it denotes the end of a period of time---"until." Used with the negative, as it is used here, it means "until" or "before," speaking also of the end of a period of time. (See William F. Arndt and F. Wilbur Gingrich, *A Greek English Lexicon of the New Testament and Other Early Christian Literature* (Chicago: The University of Chicago Press, Second Edition), pp. 334-335.

[2]The Roman Catholic view that the Greek word "*adelphos*" in this passage means "cousins" is very weak, even if we did not have Matthew 1:21. But considering the clear statement of what we have just noted in Matthew 1:21, the Roman Catholic view becomes even weaker. It is clear that Mary did not remain a perpetual virgin, as that passage says Joseph did not know (speaking of the marriage relationship) his wife Mary "until" she had brought forth her first born son (a virgin born son) and called his name Jesus. Thus, the reference in Matthew 12:47-50 and all the accompanying parallel passages referring to Christ's brothers (*adelphoi*) is speaking of the sons of Mary and Joseph, and yes, the literal brothers of Christ.

20

Who Is the Doctor?

After finishing the previous thoughts and convictions concerning Mary as an illustration of the importance of Sola Scriptura, I crawled in bed about 1:00 AM and didn't wake up till about 8:00 the next morning. After bathing, I found a note under my door from Phil. He wanted me to call him, as soon as I had rejoined the human race. I called his room, though I was not sure of the other part of his request---if I had rejoined the human race yet.

After breakfast, and after my devotions, I figured I could call the plastic surgeon in California, even though it was Sunday, and catch the doctor at home, if not at his office. I tried his home first. I really didn't care if I did get this doctor out of bed, if he was the one who made somebody look like me. After several rings, a woman answered (I assumed it was his wife), but she told me he was busy just now. I pressed the issue and replied that the matter I had to discuss with him could not wait as it pertained to one of the doctor's patients, who had stolen my identity, through the doctor's help. I used the words "stolen" and "help," because their use could even imply criminal actions by the doctor to help the criminal intentions of a patient. My words must have registered with the doctor's wife, because he was soon on the phone asking if he could help me.

"Hello, this is Dr. Flowers. How can I help you today?"

"Sir, have you had a patient whose face you completely re-constructed to make him look like someone entirely different from his previous appearance?" I asked.

"Well, I do plenty of reconstructions, for various reasons, but I did have a unique one lately, from a man who had plenty of money, but according to him not much time."

"What did he look like?" I asked, trying to see if he could identify Todd as the man.

"Well, I can't really tell you what he looked like before I began the surgery, but I could send you a picture of what he looked like when I was finished!" he informed me.

"I don't understand!" I offered.

"Well, part of our agreement was that when I was finished, I would have to return to him all my pictures of him prior to the operation. So that's what I did, and therefore I have no pictures of him now."

"Could you describe him for me?" I asked.

He gave a description that could have fit a number of guys I had known. And when I asked if he could draw a likeness, he informed me he had gotten a failing grade in art in high school. I didn't know if that was true or just an expression to tell me of his lack of artistic ability. When I asked him if he could advise an artist as he drew a picture, he declined, saying that he has worked on dozens of people since then, and without a picture, he couldn't be sure.

So I asked him, "How long ago was it that you worked on him?"

"Oh, six months ago, I suppose. I'll be glad to look up the records, if you wish. I do have the date still recorded in my records. Is something wrong?" he queried, with a shaky voice.

"Well, sir, you may have remade him into the likeness of another man!" I said, finally lowering the hammer.

"Oh, no! Do you, uh, uh, know this other man?" he asked.

"Yes, he looks just like me now!" I shocked him further.

"And worse yet," I continued, "he's trying to frame me for some crimes he has and is committing!" I said rather frankly. "And worst of all, the whole world, except my family and friends, think I am guilty. Plus, he may have killed my best friend at worst, or at best he is holding him hostage right now! And you might be guilty of criminal facilitation, which is a felony!"

There was no answer, so I asked another question.

"What name did he give to you?"

"Uh, Damion Spafford! Oh dear, what have I done?"

I told him I was not sure of what he had done, but I was sure of one thing---we needed as soon as possible an identification or the denial of an identification concerning this matter. And if his patient looks like me, he needed to contact the local police in Seminary City here on the East Coast, and inform them that there is a man who has taken my identity.

"Well, how can we make an identification when I don't have a picture of him?" he asked.

I informed him that I would send some one from Turnover News Agency to show him a picture of me.

"Turnover News Agency?" he asked in a shocked voice. "Do you mean that large conglomerate of news agencies? Do you mean this thing will hit the papers nationwide? Don't you realize they might implicate me for some wrongdoing for certain in this bizarre situation?"

I began to be concerned that his fear of getting in trouble would cause him to disavow the whole conversation we had just had, and worse yet, silence him concerning any dealings he might have had with Todd---if I was involved with Todd in this matter.

"Don't you know this story is all the over the news nationwide already?" he pled. "And what do you think such reports will do to my reputation and business?"

"It could be worse, if you do nothing!" I replied. "And besides, you are already guilty of criminal facilitation!"

21

What Does Church History
Say about Mary?

I tried to assure Dr. Powers before we parted that he had nothing to fear from me or from Turnover News Agency, if he would go to the authorities, and turn himself in, if necessary. That might keep his name out of it. All I wanted was information on the man who was trying to destroy me. Any help he could give me would be deeply appreciated. I assured him that someone would be by his home within a few hours to show him a picture of me to help us get to the bottom of the mystery man's original identity. He promised he would cooperate, but begged again for anonymity in the process.

It was the lunch hour by the time I got off the phone with Dr. Powers. I was eager to confirm what I already knew. Maybe then, the authorities would believe me, when I said I had seen a man in my hospital room who looked like me! But that still didn't put me any closer to being able to confirm that Todd was the mystery man. But, if he was not Todd, who could he be?

Knowing that time would soon answer these questions, hopefully, I decided to take another step in my study on Roman Catholicism. In my last meditation I had seen what Scripture says about Mary compared to the Roman Catholic Church's belief at the time of the Reformation and beyond. We had concluded that the changes took place (even some further changes from the time of the Reformation to the present), because the Roman Catholic Church does not believe in Sola Scriptura. But it was allowed to free wheel in its doctrinal affirmations due to its multi-source authority structure. This practice not only added various beliefs to the doctrines of the church, but even caused changes to the doctrinal teachings of the Bible.

The Historical Development of the Doctrine of Mary

Though I did not have the time or the space to do a complete study of the historical development of the doctrine of Mary in Roman Catholic history, I decided to give a brief survey. I would ask the reader to remember the previous study, especially the pristine simple statements of the Bible itself about Mary. The question I faced now was not, how did the changes take place? I had already said that these changes could only take place because of the multi-source authority structure of the Roman Catholic Church---the Bible plus so many supposed added authorities. Now I was asking the reader to note the changes that did take place on the basis of the Roman Catholic Church's authority base.

The Protoevangelium of James of the Second Century

Historical research shows that there was no special interest in the exaltation of Mary in the first century of the history of Christianity. It wasn't until the second century, when an pseudepigraphical book, which was titled *Protoevangelium of James*, appeared, that the picture of Mary began to change. This book was written about 150 AD with the author claiming to be James, the brother of Christ. This book supposedly details Mary's early family, her birth, her engagement to Joseph, the annunciation of the angel, and the birth of Christ. But the book was not recognized as belonging to the canon; that is, it was not recognized to be an inspired New Testament book. Yet the book did become a springboard for future interest in the development of the Marian legend.

The Patristic Writings concerning Mary

Most of the Patristic writings (writings of the early church fathers in the second century) did not even mention Mary, and those who spoke of her did not teach the later doctrine of Mary, and they certainly did not have the views which are promulgated today by the Roman Catholic Church. Understandably, and rightfully so, the main concern of the second century writings of the church fathers was the virgin birth of Christ.

The Influence of the Nestorian Controversy

It is well known by any student of church history that the fifth century was the period when the doctrine of Christ was in full debate. How do the human and divine natures of Christ relate to one another? One position in the discussion, though properly rejected, was the Nestorian view. It had emphasized the distinction of the two natures so as to conclude falsely that Christ was two persons. Nestorius did not want to give to Mary the title of "Mother of God" (theotokos). He argued that Mary was only the mother of Christ, to whom the person of the Word (the divine being) had been united. The Council of Ephesus rejected the Nestorian view in favor of the belief that Mary was the Mother of God (*theotokos*). The reason for the rejection of Nestorianism was the conviction that they must safeguard the unity of the two natures of Christ in one person.

Though the decision of the council in the fifth century was not to advance the doctrine of Mary, it did, nonetheless, promote the Marian devotion. There was also a renewed interest in the pseudepigraphal writing *Protoevangelium of James*. But not all of the church fathers were in agreement with the desire of some to exalt Mary. Jerome (early fifth century) said that such exaltation of Mary was "delirious nonsense." But some seemed bound and determined to continue the elevation and exaltation of Mary.

The Barbarian Invasions
of the Fifth and Tenth Centuries

Another influence on the growing development of the exaltation of Mary, as well as the rest of the Roman Catholic theology and practice, was the Barbarian invasions of the fifth and tenth centuries. These invasions came in strong force, as hordes of pagan warriors came down over the Roman Empire from the north. The first of these invasions (fifth century) brought a new culture to the territory of the old Roman Empire, and the church became the bridge between the old culture of the empire and the new culture of the barbarians, though there was a cost involved. As the church sought the "conversion" of the these barbarians, there came a capitulation to their religious thinking, as Christian doctrine was recast in pagan forms, in order to win the people to the church. The following thoughts from Christopher Henry Dawson, who himself was a Roman Catholic, tell the story.

As Christianity faced the barbarians in the fifth century, it seemed hopeless, as far as the church was concerned, because of the strength of the barbaric warriors and the ignorance of the simple peasants. It must be admitted that there was nothing in the culture or social traditions of the barbarians which could help them to understand the religious thought and the moral ideals of the civilized Christian world, which they had invaded.[1] Clearly, though, the empire had fallen, and the church had survived, but the task the church faced was spreading the faith among the barbarians.[2] This became a missionary age, and the Roman Catholic Church saw the "conversion" of many of the barbarian tribes.[3]

The church was able to do such a work of "missions," because, even though the new barbarian kingdoms had taken over the military and political functions of the empire, all else, such as education and culture, moral authority, and the care of the people fell to the church.[4] Thus, in the passing of time there came an assimilation of barbarism and Christianity, which tended to create a new social unity, for as the barbarians converted to Christianity, they also acquired elements of the higher culture, while the Christian society was gradually losing touch with the traditions of Roman culture and was also being paganized.[5]

The Christian culturalization process of the barbarians, therefore, had to begin from a very low level with poor materials, the barbarians. When the first great step had been accomplished, which was their conversion [though some have questioned such wholesale conversions], it was only the beginning of a much longer and more arduous struggle to overcome the inherent barbarism of the Christianized barbarians.[6] The peasants, more so even than the kings of the barbarians, were divided between the two traditions, but they all to some extent were still bound to the old pagan customs, long after they had become nominal or even supposedly devout members of the Christian society.[7] How was the church to defeat the old pagan customs, and establish Christianity? The church solved this problem by providing a Christian ceremony to take the place of each of the heathen ones.[8]

It must be admitted that the barbarians could not assimilate the profound theological metaphysics of Augustine or the great teachers of the Byzantine world. But they could plug into mythology (saints, and saint worship, relics and miracles), which the church allowed, in order that they might fuse the Christian faith and ethics to the barbarian tradition.[9] For centuries to follow, as barbarian invasions continued, even through the tenth century, the paganization of the church continued, as paganism remained strong and threatened the church from within and without by masses of uninstructed and half-converted peasants and barbarians, who had found themselves Christians, as it were, without knowing it, owing to the conversion of their landlords and chieftains.[10]

This period, too, due to the influence of pagan barbarianism, expanded and imbedded the exaltation of Mary into the Roman Catholic doctrine, as she became very helpful to the church in relating to a people from pagan backgrounds, all of which had female deities.

The Feasts of Mary

All of these influences came together to create, promote and expand the interest and elevation of the Mary enthusiasts. In time there were also feasts to Mary, which multiplied after the Council of Ephesus.

1. The Feast of Mary's Bodily Assumption into Heaven

   This feast was celebrated by many of the churches from the beginning of the sixth century. It centered on the assumption that Christ would not allow his mother's body at death to suffer the corruption of the flesh. He must have taken her bodily into heaven and spared her from rotting in a human grave. This idea was not from any Biblical evidence, but from a human assumption.

2. The Feast of the Annunciation

   This feast was observed from the middle of the seventh century, to remember the hour of the angel's announcement to Mary that she would be the mother of Christ.

3. The Feast of the Nativity of Mary

   Observed in Rome by the middle of the seventh century.

4. The Feast of the Conception of Mary

   This feast began in the east in the seventh century, but was unknown in the west until the eleventh century.

Faith in Mary's Power of Intercession

Germanus (eighth century), patriarch of Constantinople, popularized the idea that Mary had a maternal influence over God, and it was believed that she could turn away God's wrath, making her a mediatrix between God and man.

Summary of Our Historical Study Thus Far

Thus, by the beginning of the eighth century the elevation of Mary was well advanced and far from the truth of Mary as set forth in the Scriptures. Where in the Scripture are the feasts to Mary? Where is the doctrine of Mary's bodily assumption, as even the Roman Catholic Church calls it an assumption? Where is the idea in the Bible that Mary has a maternal influence on God the Father, which would be so great that she was considered to be a co-redemtrix? What about the Biblical doctrine which clearly teaches that there is one mediator between God and man, and that man is Christ Jesus (I Timothy 2:5)?

My historical survey was not finished, but I felt I had to stop, as I was feeling the weariness of the previous evening. I determined I would catch a nap, and then see what Mac had found out. I probably would have slept more than an hour and a half, had I not been interrupted by a phone call from Phil. I immediately asked him the key question before us.

"Do you have any leads or even any ideas concerning where we can find Dink?"

"Well, if you feel up to it, I was just going out on a hunch---no more than a hunch---to see if we might get a break or two on this case."

He didn't say what his hunch was---he didn't have to! I was ready to trace any lead---good, bad or indifferent!

"What time are we leaving?" I asked.

"In about fifteen minutes!" he replied. "I'll come by your room. I have something for you to wear!"

I had no idea what he was talking about, but I was eager to do anything to find Dink!

[1]Christopher Henry Dawson, *Medieval Religion and Other Essays* (London: Sheed and Ward, 1934), p. 7.

[2]Christopher Henry Dawson, *The Formation of Christendom* (New York: Sheed and Ward, 1967), p. 156.

[3]Ibid., p. 173.

[4]Christopher Henry Dawson, *Religion and the Rise of Western Culture* (New York: Sheed and Ward, 1950), p. 29.

[5]Ibid.

[6]*Formation*, p. 161.

[7]Ibid., p. 172.

[8]Christopher Henry Dawson, *The Making of Europe* (New York: Sheed and Ward, 1945), p. 202.

[9]*Religion and the Rise* (New York: Sheed and Ward), p. 33.

[10]*Medieval Religion,* p. 33.

[11]*Rise of Western Culture*, p. 32.

22

Could It Be That the Search Has Ended?

I discovered when Phil entered my motel room, that he had brought me a disguise. He laughed, a kindly laugh, and told me if I went out like I was dressed, anyone who had even seen a picture of me could recognize me. And even worse, anyone who even knew me could recognize me a mile away because of the clothes I was wearing. I had to admit that I was pretty standard in what I wore---every day.

So I donned the clothes he had brought, which made me resemble a reporter more than a preacher or teacher! No necktie, no dress jacket, no British-style driving cap, etc., but just a normal leisure jacket with a baseball type cap. I had to admit that I felt under-dressed, but he was right. But even beyond the change of clothes, he gave me a wig to put on---not a big one, but a blond one, which was again a far cry from my brownish-black hair. I was certain the wig would be easily recognized as a wig, but when placed correctly on my head, it looked like a real head of hair.

And he gave me a pair of sunglasses to wear. He said he had noticed I wore no glasses, so the glasses (especially sun glasses) would change my appearance immensely. Then he had me look into the mirror, as he told me that not even my wife could recognize me now. I had to admit it--- he was right---I certainly looked different! I didn't even recognize myself. Now, we were really ready to go.

As we entered the car, and began to back out of the parking slot at the motel, I asked him where we were going. He countered with a question.

"Were you ever aware of any girlfriends Todd used to have, when he was in Seminary City?" he asked.

As I scratched my head, I replied, "I knew Todd had been married some years ago, but his marriage broke up while he was in a pastorate. But beyond that I never knew about any girlfriend or friends."

"Well, our investigation shows that he was very close to a young lady some years ago, and that she wanted marriage, but he didn't. She was really crazy about him, and would have done almost anything for him---legally or illegally. My hunch is that Todd may be hiding out at her place here in town, and that also might be the place where Dink is being held captive!"

My heart began to pound! I didn't want to get my hopes built up too high, but we were not just going to cruise around to see if we might turn something up---we had a real lead, and we might find Dink today---very soon! I guess Phil saw or anticipated my state of mind, and so he cautioned me not to get too pumped up. It might be a false alarm, but it was worth checking out.

I studied Phil quietly for a moment. He and other investigative reporters have their ways, I admitted. But who would have taken him to be in that profession. He was humble and unassuming. He could be in a room with you in a crowd for a long period of time, and you would never notice him. He was quiet, but strong and confident, when you got to know him. He was not boisterous, nor arrogant, nor pushy, nor demeaning, nor insulting. He was polite and courteous---a real gentleman. I guess that was what made him a good investigator. Immediately, a person felt he could be trusted. He was an average-sized guy, with an average subdued personality, but I was discovering that nothing got past him.

After driving about fifteen minutes, we pulled onto a back street in the lower middle class part of town. He stopped, and pointed out a house down in the middle of the block. There was one car parked in the driveway---no garage. It looked quiet around the house and the other houses in the block---something understandable in the middle of the afternoon with children at school and parents at work.

Then Phil reached for his car phone, and to my surprise, he called the police! He spoke to the dispatcher in a muffled gruff voice.

"I think I can tell you where you can find Dr. Ira Pointer!"

This statement was followed by his disclosure of the address of the house that we were watching, and the address of the place where the woman worked. I almost dropped my teeth, until I saw what he was doing. He was going to let the police do the work. And sure enough, several police cars were on the scene in just a few minutes. They surrounded the house from all sides, just to be sure their suspect could not get away. Two of the officers went to the front door and knocked. But no one answered. So they waited until another police car drove up, and a woman got out. The two officers with her escorted her to the door of the house! Phil noted that it was the girl friend. She made no attempt to stop the officers from entering the house. And a few minutes later, they brought the man who looked like me out the front door in handcuffs!

As I sat and watched, I was sure the officers thought they had captured me---the dangerous and violent lunatic, and I could already envision the talking heads on the news programs announcing the great catch. But then an ambulance appeared and my heart pounded. Was this evidence that Dink was in the house? I couldn't stay in the car! Phil tried to stop me, but not even a Green Bay Packer linebacker could have stopped my run to the house. I was glad I had a disguise on, but as I ran I considered the probable certainty that they might try to keep me out---unless I told them who I was.

Just as I arrived a few steps from the door, they brought out a body. It appeared to be emaciated and lifeless---but it was Dink. Tears began to pour down my cheeks. Poor Dink---it appeared obvious that he was near death, if not already dead. It was apparent also they had been starving him to death, or that he hadn't been able to eat. It also seemed certain that he had not been getting any medical care.

I asked, "Is the man you are bringing out dead?"

Though the medic looked at me strangely, as if he was wondering who I might be, he replied, "No, he's barely alive! But I can't tell you if he will make it!"

I couldn't go on with the disguise, so I ripped off the disguise---the hair, the glasses, etc. I told the officers who were standing there that I was Dr. Ira Pointer, and this man, Dink, was my best friend, and I had to go with him to the hospital! The police were flabbergasted!

"I thought we already took you to the police station!" one of them said, as they stood there puzzled.

"That's what I have been trying to tell you! There was a man impersonating me, but no one listened! Now you know I was telling the truth. I am not a nut case, as you supposed, but the man who looks like me has been trying to frame me and ruin my life. But I will explain all of that later. Right now, my best friend is dying and I must go with him in the ambulance to the hospital! Please call his wife, and then go get her and take her to the hospital so she can be with her husband in this crucial hour!"

My takeover attitude, and my immediate ability to give a phone number and address from memory, may very well have made my case. With some remaining reluctance, and with an accompanying officer, they agreed to let me be with Dink as they took him to the hospital. As I crawled into the ambulance and got a closer look at Dink, I was further shocked. Not only was he emaciated from lack of nourishment, but he was also battered in the face from the result of the explosion. He was unconscious, which was probably best, so I just rode and prayed, while we moved towards the hospital.

I was surprised again when Janie and Terry were both at the hospital when we arrived. I learned later that Phil had contacted them both from his car. We all stood and watched and then followed as they carried Dink's frail body into the emergency room. Then we all broke down and cried like babies, as we stood together in a three-way hug. Words were out of place, because the presence of Christ was with us, and the unity of our hearts in Christ, evidenced by our sobs and tears and silent embrace, gave more comfort to us all than a thousand words could give at this time.

We were all grateful that one battle was over, but in my heart I knew there were others to come, before things were back to normal. But for now, the only battle that mattered was Dink's battle for life!

23

Who Is Our Mediator and Redeemer?

I knew that the next few days would be quite hectic. Dink was hanging between life and death. The doctors told us that if we had not found him, he would have been dead within a day. He had been suffering not only from starvation, but also from internal injuries from the explosion. We would rotate the vigil at the hospital, in case Dink's condition changed quickly. I would man the night hours, and Terry and Janie would stay during the day. Since the nights were quiet and lonely, I passed the time as I continued my study on Roman Catholicism.

I had been tracing the development of the church's beliefs about Mary, and had journeyed as far as the Middle Ages. I had presented the teaching of the New Testament about Mary. I had concluded from the evidence that in the following years, especially from the third century on, the Marian theology had taken wings for various reasons, one being the barbarian invasions and their takeover of the Roman territory in the fifth century. It was not because of anything in Scripture.

The Development of the Doctrine of Mary
Continues through the Middle Ages

The Story of Theophilus

It was in the eighth century that there came another impetus for the elevation of Mary through what is known as

The Story of Theophilus. It was a fictitious story about a man who gave his soul to the devil, to get a certain post, and then wished to repent and be forgiven of his sins. He sought Mary's aid, which she graciously gave, and the devil was forced to free his soul---all because of the intercession of Mary.

Thus, the bypassing of Christ, the only mediator between God and man (I Timothy 2:5), is shown to be acceptable, and Mary now becomes the redemptrix of captives, the refuge of sinners, and a mediator between God and man. This legend was eventually presented in a play, where Christ was pictured as the stern and threatening judge, whose heart was softened only by the intercession and pleas of Mary.

Bernard of Clairvaux

Bernard of Clairvaux, a man of the twelfth century, was one of the most influential promoters of the doctrine of Mary during the Middle Ages. His sermons, titled "In Praise of Virgin Mary," which set forth an all-powerful Mary, were extremely influential in theology and in the popular devotion throughout the Roman Catholic Church.

Bernard's view of Mary was quite clear---she had a powerful role and part in the redemption of mankind. His saying that God had willed everything through Mary was a maxim that continued for centuries to follow, even to our times. He was concerned that both men and women might fear Christ, in that Christ is also their God and judge. What it then boils down to, is that man needs a mediator with the Mediator, and that subsidiary mediator was Mary. Of course, all of this sounds very nice, but not one ounce of it is found in the Bible.

The Immaculate Conception

The Immaculate Conception is not the same as the virgin birth, as some may mistakenly think. The virgin birth is clearly taught in Scripture, that is, that Christ was born of a virgin. The Immaculate Conception pertains to Mary, as it is the belief that Mary was preserved from original sin by the power of divine omnipotence.[1] It is believed that sanctifying grace was infused into her soul from the instant of her conception in the womb. Strangely enough, Bernard of Clairvaux was an opponent of this doctrine, as he denied it and called it a superstition. It was not, however, because of anything in Scripture. He did allow that Mary was sanctified in the womb, and remained sinless throughout her life, which is not stated in Scripture. Anselm also opposed the doctrine of the Immaculate Conception.

William of Ware (early fourteenth century) bolstered the argument for the acceptance of this doctrine by repeating a legend that had come into existence in England. The legend said that Bernard of Clairvaux had appeared to a layman soon after his death in a radiant white garment, but it had one stain on it---his error concerning the doctrine of the Immaculate Conception.

Thomas Aquinas, the premier Roman Catholic theologian of the Middle Ages, opposed the Immaculate Conception, because he thought it would detract from Christ's redemptive work. He did agree that Mary was sanctified in the womb, which made her the greatest of all saints in history.

Boneventure opposed the Immaculate Conception also, but he gave some role to Mary in the redemptive work of Christ at the cross, when he said that she consented to sacrifice her son. His statement, and others like this, were still instrumental in promoting Mary as the co-redemptrix of the human race.

Other Influences upon the Exaltation of Mary

1. Hail Mary

   This became a prayer that people were to pray to Mary, and the present form dates back to 1568.[2]

   Hail, Mary! Full of Grace,
   The Lord is with Thee;
   Blessed art thou among women,
   And blessed is the fruit of thy womb, Jesus.
   Holy Mary, Mother of God,
   Pray for us sinners,
   Now, and at the hour of our death.
   Amen.

   The real error of this prayer is clear. Nowhere in Scripture are we ever taught to pray to Mary. Clearly in Scripture Christ is set forth as the only mediator between God and man.

2. The Rosary

   This is the name of a devotion and the chain of beads used for counting the prayers. This means of praying is believed to have arisen in the fifteenth century, featuring Mary as somewhat central in it.[3]

5. The Angelus

This consisted of Hail Marys and prayers to Mary three times a day at the ringing of the Angelus bells. It began in 1318.[4]

6. Supposed Visions, etc. which promoted Mary

The mystical aspect of this whole doctrine (no grounding in the Bible) was manifested by supposed visions and revelations of Mary. This had taken place in earlier centuries, but increased, becoming more common later in the Middle Ages.

The Holy House of Loreto in the same century (fourteenth) was believed to have been transported through the air from Nazareth, and therefore was thought to have miraculous powers.

The Divine Comedy by Dante (fourteenth century) gives us a good understanding of the beliefs that were forming concerning Mary during the Middle Ages. This work shows her to have influence throughout the entire universe---on earth, in purgatory, in heaven and in hell.

I looked up, after finishing this section of thought, and was shocked to find that it was close to midnight. I came on at 7:00 PM and stood watch till 7:00 AM. I had not gotten much sleep, since the events of finding Dink, and the arrest of the mystery man, and the long time of explaining all the events to the police. I had not had the chance even to read the daily paper to see how they were handling all these events.

So, when I saw a paper lying on the couch of the waiting room, I thought I would at least skim a few articles. I was shocked at the headline, which read: FUGITIVE SEMINARY PROFESSOR FOUND WITH STARVING FRIEND! I immediately wondered what they meant by that statement! First, it was wrong. I had not been found with my starving friend. I arrived at the scene and was part of the reason that he was found, and I did not get to the actual scene at the house until the police were bringing the mystery man and Dink out of the house. Second, that statement could very easily leave the impression I had been the one keeping Dink in captivity!

And, third, the police---but that's another story! It had taken me several hours to get the police straightened out concerning my innocence! I knew that Phil would probably have his story in all the Turnover papers, but I wondered if the Seminary City paper would ever get it right.

I stretched out on the couch for a nap, hoping that would relieve me from the continuing confusion and chaos. How could anyone get anything so confused?

---

[1]Robert C. Broderick, *The Catholic Encyclopedia* (Nashville: Thomas Nelson Publishers, 1975), p. 288.

[2]Ibid., p. 254.

[3]Ibid., p. 529.

[4] Ibid., p. 37.

24

What Is the Doctrine
of the Immaculate Conception?

My nap on the couch was disturbed not only by the headlines, but also by the doctor's coming out again to give me an update on Dink. The report was the same---he was holding his own! I went in, as I did at the regular visiting intervals in intensive care, and prayed with him. Though he didn't appear to be conscious, who really knew what he heard and understood? They were feeding him intravenously, so he didn't need to be awake for the intake of nourishment.

The walls of the room were filled with cards and letters of encouragement from students, friends, faculty members and churches where he had ministered. I read a few of them, and so many spoke of Dink's having led them to the Lord. That was his gift---evangelism. He never met a stranger, and he was so unassuming and direct and humble that he disarmed a person immediately, so he could in his Columbo style and manner present to them the gospel---and they would listen. I even found a large card from Reggie Falayla---one of his old buddies from the gang days, another person Dink had led to Christ.

Tears welled up in my eyes, as I remembered all we had been through. Dink had been a friend that the Scriptures spoke of---one who sticks closer than a brother! I began to cry and pray even more earnestly than before, as I tried to realize what my life would have been like without him, or what it would be like in the future were the Lord to take him home to heaven. I was submissive to the Lord, as I prayed, "Thy will be done!" I knew if God took him, He was still working all things after the counsel of His own will (Ephesians 1:11), and I would continue to be submissive! But that didn't mean I wouldn't miss him! There would never be another "Dink" in my life! He was that kind of a man and friend!

As I went back to the waiting room, I tried to sleep, but sleep would not come near my body this night. So I decided to pursue my study of Roman Catholicism, and try to finish my thoughts concerning Mary.

The Reformation Period to 1850

The Reformers agreed with Mary's godliness and life of faith, accepting only what was in the Scriptures. They certainly rejected the idea of a co-redemptrix.

The Council of Trent (1545-1563) continued to defend Mary and the ideas about her role as a co-redemptrix and intercessor.

The French School of the Roman Catholic Church initiated what was called "true devotion" to the Blessed Virgin, which required an absolute surrender to Mary. This was the only effective way, they believed, to come to Christ. If we came directly to Christ, He would see our self-love and not receive us, but Mary would get to His weak side, so we then could be received by Him.

The Rationalism of the eighteenth century subdued some of the Mary theology and practice. Cardinal Lambertini, an admired scholar, who became Pope Benedict XIV in 1740, attacked the exaggerations of the Marian piety, including such ideas that Mary gave orders in heaven, or that one should defend the Immaculate

Conception even to the shedding of blood. During this period also (eighteenth century), enlightenment thinking stifled the Marian feasts in some places, and lessened the interest in the theology of Mary, etc.

In Italy the Marian devotion was fueled by the Redemptorists, including especially the book by St. Alphonsus Ligouri (died 1787). His book, titled *The Glories of Mary*, defended the Immaculate Conception and Mary's universal mediation of grace. He also repeated and promoted the medieval thinking that Mary alone knows how to appease an angry God by her prayers.

1850 to 1950

We will deal with the doctrine of Mary in this section by taking the individual doctrines concerning her, and at times we will even go back into previous periods of church history to bring the doctrine of Mary up to date.

The Immaculate Conception

This doctrine states that Mary, the Mother of Jesus, was free from original sin from the moment of her conception. This is not the same as the virgin birth!

In 1496 the Feast of the Immaculate Conception was approved by Pope Sixtus IV.

In the sixteenth century the Council of Trent excluded Mary from its decree of the universality of original sin.

In 1661 Pope Alexander VII forbade attacks on the doctrine of the Immaculate Conception, so the Dominicans (who had opposed the doctrine) changed their views.

Interest in the doctrine of the Immaculate Conception faded until the early nineteenth century, when on December

17, 1830, St. Catherine Laboure claimed to have had a vision of the Immaculate Conception. The vision was surrounded by a frame with the words, "O Mary, conceived without sin, pray for us who have recourse to thee." This was followed by a voice that commanded Catherine to make a medal picturing the vision. The medal was named "Miraculous," because miracles were attributed to it. Plus, it stimulated new interest in the doctrine of Mary.

Pope Pius IX (died 1878) sought, after consultation with 603 bishops, a definition of the Immaculate Conception. Fifty-six bishops opposed the definition. But still in a papal bull of December 8, 1854, Pope Pius IX decreed that "The most Blessed Virgin Mary was, from the first moment of her conception, by singular grace and privilege of almighty God and in view of the merits of Christ Jesus the Savior of the human race, preserved immune from all stain of original sin, that this is revealed by God and, therefore, firmly and constantly to be believed by all the faithful."

Marian Shrines

In the years that followed, this led to a number of supposed appearances by Mary, where shrines were then built to honor her in such places as Lourdes, France; Knock, Ireland; Fatima, Portugal; Czestochowa, Poland; Guadalupe, Mexico; and Montserrat, Spain.

Mary's Bodily Assumption

This is the doctrine which assumes that Mary entered heaven without dying, because Christ would not allow His mother's body to corrupt in the grave. Pope Pius XII (died

1958) was the primary figure in the defining the doctrine of the bodily assumption of Mary into heaven. Her crowning glory, he said, was to be preserved from the corruption of the tomb, and like her son before her, to conquer death and to be raised body and soul to the glory of heaven to shine as the Queen at the right hand of her Son, the immortal King of ages. But even still the statement was uncertain in many areas. Did Mary die? What was the manner of the assumption? What was the time of the assumption? Pope Pius XII also consecrated the entire world to the Immaculate Heart of Mary in 1942.

As my eyes were wilting at this point, I put my books and papers down, and then, before I knew it, someone was gently shaking me to wake me up. It was Terry. I don't know how long I had slept, but it was 7:00 AM, and time to change shifts. I gave Terry and Janie the latest on Dink, which wasn't much. Then Terry offered that Dr. Harbour had called last night, and said he wanted to see me. He said to make an appointment as soon as possible.

Though I was glad to hear this, I still couldn't figure out why he hadn't been to see Dink. I asked Janie if he had called her, and she said he had never contacted her since any of this had happened. I was mulling this over in my mind, when Terry handed me the morning paper. As usual I took it out of its cover, opened it, and was absolutely shocked to see the headline. I said out loud, "Here we go again! Who would have believed it!"

25

Who Would Have Believed This?

If the headline I had read just a few hours ago in yesterday morning's paper shocked me, the headline in this day's paper floored me. It bluntly and boldly declared:

Seminary Professor in Hot Water Again---
Accused of Planning Explosion!

The article began by giving the confession of the mystery man that he was Todd Shelton. It continued with the ridiculous claim that I was the primary perpetrator of the explosion for the purpose of trying to kill Dink. I, supposedly, had contacted him because I had grown jealous of Dink, but also ashamed of his embarrassing ways. Todd said he didn't care too much for Dink either, and this is why he decided to cooperate with my idea!

The plan that I had concocted, he said, was to publish a book on Roman Catholicism. He was to arrange for its publication in my name, but he was to have plastic surgery, so that he would look like me, when he made such arrangements. He said he needed a new identity, anyway, so why not look like me. I had figured, he claimed, that would get me off the hook, if the police accused me of the crime. In the meantime, he could slip out of town, and change his identity again. I was then supposed to have lured Dink into the apartment building on the pretense that someone had published the book in my name, and we were trying to solve the crime. There in the apartment building the explosion would take place, and it was supposed to kill Dink. I purposefully was not in the same room as Dink when the explosion took place, so I would not be killed.

The problem came when Dink survived the blast, and I suffered a concussion or some sort of head injury, and had to go to the hospital. Todd then said, therefore, that he had taken Dink to his girl friend's house. Then another problem surfaced, according to his story, when I suffered a lapse of memory, and forgot that there was a man in town who looked like me. When he tried secretly to visit me in the hospital, to discuss what to do next, I began to rant and rave about a man being there who looked like me. That's why he fled from my room each time! He had only come to find out what we were going to do next, but after two visits, he gave up trying. I was too far out of it.

Then, in my mental weakness, I thought someone was after me, and thus I broke out of the hospital. He traced me to my office, and when he tried to see me there, I attacked him and stabbed him with a knife. I would have killed him, according to Todd, had he not been able to break away and flee the scene once more. It was then that I was supposed to have regained my memory, and recalled that he had Dink. Todd claimed further that when he was found harboring a starving Dink, he was only doing what I had instructed him to do!

I then called Mac Turnover, according to Todd, but I was not fully honest with him, because I did not tell him the whole story. I, supposedly, had told Mac that Todd was the one trying to kill Dink. On that basis, Mac decided to help me try to find Dink. But Todd claimed that I really wanted to find Dink, so I could finish the job of eliminating him.

Thus, Phil met me and took me to the motel, and unbeknownst to me, while I rested, Phil found out where Todd might be keeping Dink. He decided to take me to that place, but he didn't get a chance to tell me until we were on our way. At this point, I didn't know what to do. I couldn't go ahead and kill Dink in front of Phil. Todd said that I probably hoped that I could get into the house without Phil, so I could do my dirty work. But when Phil called the police, Todd said I probably figured getting rid of Dink was hopeless at this point. Thus, he said, I decided to play along as the great hero, who had come to rescue Dink, and blame the whole scheme on him.

I couldn't believe it! What a liar! Surely no one would believe him. Or would they? Knowing the press reporters and the television media, I felt sick, as I began to ask questions. Could I expect the police to come and pick me up soon, to take me to the police station for questioning, and then would I be incarcerated before the day was over? Would I be deluged by the media any moment to be grilled by them, as if I was really guilty? Just when I thought it was all over, my adversary had turned the table on me, so it seemed---again!

What should I do? Stay and face the music and fight the accusations? Or run again? Who now would believe my story? Would Mac and Phil think I had betrayed them? Would Dr. Harbour believe me? What would happen to Dink, if I ran? Wouldn't I miss his funeral, if he died, and I had run? But would I even be free to go any place, if I stayed? They won't let you out of jail, even to go to a funeral! But even more, if I ran, where would I go?

26

Was Mary a Coredemptrix?

As I mulled over my choices, I decided I really had no choice. I must stay and fight the false accusations of Todd. Perhaps, no one will believe him, anyway. If I ran, it surely would make me look guilty. Maybe, too, I could pay the bail, if they arrested me. That would allow me to be free, while the police tried to figure it all out, and I tried to help them.

But before I left the hospital, I showed the article to Terry. I thought she was going to have a heart attack---at least a small fit! Of course, then Janie wanted to know what we were so demonstrative about. When she saw it, she probably would have choked Todd (figuratively speaking), had he been in the room.

"Who would ever believe that!" she exclaimed.

Feeling better about the matter, I left the hospital. But I was met by flashing lights, pulling me over, as I drove home. When I had stopped, a southern-talking policeman approached my car.

"You Dr. Pointer?" he asked.

"Yes, sir!" I responded, as politely as I knew how.

"Can you tell me where yer a goin'?" he asked.

"Home, sir," I replied again, with great humility.

"Boy, you're in a heapa trouble!" he said with great seriousness.

"What for?" I asked, remaining calm.

"Boy, this ain't no playground pick-me-up game, you got yerself inta!"

"You mean, pick-up game?" I softly corrected him.

"Boy, you know what I'm a talkin' bout!" he responded, looking over his sunglasses.

I could have laughed at his seriousness in the midst of all the humor he brought to such a supposedly serious job.

"Are you going to take me into the police station?" I asked, trying not to laugh.

"You sure hit bingo on that one, son!" he informed me.

Thus, off to the station we went. I was allowed one phone call, before they locked me up. So I called Mac, and explained the whole mess to him. He couldn't believe Todd's story either. I praised the Lord for a friend in Mac. He said not to worry, that he would have one of his top lawyers there before the day was over, and he would not only defend me, but he would, if his lawyer could, get me out on bail today. As it turned out, they needed more evidence to charge me, which they said might come in the future. But for now, I was free to go. I got home just in time to eat a bite of supper, say hello to the kids, and head off to the hospital again to watch over Dink through the night!

After checking on Dink, and seeing he was still unconscious, I made my way back to my books and notebooks, to pursue my study further. I had traced the doctrine of Mary in many areas---too many to repeat at this point. I had just one area left---the claim of the Roman Catholic Church that Mary was a co-redemptrix---that is a co-redeemer with her son, Jesus Christ. This was a particularly troubling doctrine to me, because there was not one speck of evidence in the New Testament to that effect. In fact, there was much evidence that Christ is the only redeemer. But, first, I wanted to note what the Roman Catholic Church said about Mary as a co-redemptrix. I decided just to list the numerous quotes I had found that stated this conviction of the church.

Statements of Various Popes about Mary

LEO XIII (1878-1903) said the following about Mary:

> She was so intimately associated with the mystery of human salvation and is just as closely associated with the distribution of graces. (Encyclical Adjutricem Populi, September 5, 1895)

> She knew beforehand all these agonies [of the cross]; she knew them and saw them. When she professed herself the handmaid of the Lord for the mother's office, and when, at the foot of the altar, she offered up her whole self with her child Jesus,...she took her part in the painful expiation offered by her son for the sins of the world...As we contemplate him in the last and most piteous of these mysteries, we see that there stood by the cross of Jesus his mother, who...generously offered her own Son to Divine Justice and in her own heart died with him, stabbed by the sword of sorrow. (Encyclical Jucunda Semper, September 8, 1894)

POPE PIUS X (1903-1914) said the following (the underlining is mine):

> Mary prepared the victim for sacrifice by conceiving and bearing Him; she offered Him on the altar at the appointed time; she participated in the redemption by a community of pain and will

between herself and Christ. (Encyclical <u>Ad Diem Illum</u>, 36, 1903-1904)

<u>Mary has merited for us congruously [in agreement], as they say, what Christ has merited for us condignly [appropriately]</u>. (*Ibid.*)

POPE BENEDICT XV (1914-1922) said the following:

Thus, she suffered and all but died along with her son suffering and dying; thus for the salvation of men she abdicated the rights of a mother toward her son, and insofar as it was hers to do, she <u>immolated [to kill or offer a sacrifice] the Son to placate God's justice, so that she herself may justly be said to have redeemed together with Christ the human race.</u> (Apostolic Letter <u>Inter Sodalacia</u>, 1918, 182)

POPE PIUS XI (1922-39) said the following:

By giving us Christ the redeemer and by rearing him, and by offering him at the foot of the cross as victim for our sins..., <u>Mary became and is known as reparatrix</u> [one who affects repairs or makes amends]. (Encyclical <u>Miserentissimus Redemptor</u>, 1928, 178)

A prayer of Pope Pius XI was "O Mother of love and mercy who, when thy sweetest Son was consummating the redemption of the human race on the altar of the cross, didst stand next to him, <u>suffering with him as a coredemptrix</u>..." (April, 28, 1935)

POPE PIUS XII (1939-1958) said of Mary:

> It was she, the second Eve who, free from all
> sin....and always most intimately united with her
> Son, offered him on Golgotha to the eternal Father
> for all the children of Adam, sin-stained by his
> unhappy fall, and her mother's rights and mother's
> love were included in the holocaust." (Marian
> Epilogue of the Encyclical *Mystici Corporis Christi*,
> 1943, 247)

Statements of Vatican II about Mary

The sacred Scriptures of both the Old and New
Testament, as well as ancient tradition, show the role of
the Mother of the Savior in the economy of salvation in
an ever clearer light and propose it as something to be
probed into. (*Documents of Vatican II*, p. 87)

It is no wonder, then, that the usage prevailed among
the holy Fathers whereby they called the mother of God
entirely holy and free from all stain of sin, fashioned by
the Holy Spirit into a kind of new substance and new
creature. (*Ibid.*, p. 88)

The knot of Eve's disobedience was untied by Mary's
obedience. (*Ibid.*)

Finally, preserved free from all guilt of original sin, the
Immaculate Virgin, was taken up body and soul into
heavenly glory upon the completion of her earthly
sojourn. She was exalted by the Lord as Queen of all...
(*Ibid.*, p. 90)

By her maternal charity, Mary cares for the brethren of her Son who still journey on earth surrounded by dangers and difficulties, until they are led to their happy fatherland. Therefore the Blessed Virgin is invoked by the Church under the titles of <u>Advocate</u>, <u>Auxiliatrix</u>, <u>Adjutrix</u>, and <u>Mediatrix</u>. These, however, are to be understood that they neither take away from nor add anything to the dignity and efficacy of Christ the one Mediator. (*Ibid*, 91-92)

For taken up to heaven, she did not lay aside this saving role, but by her manifold acts of intercession continues to win for us gifts of eternal salvation. (*Ibid*, p. 91)

At this point my eyes began to droop, and I decided to summarize what I had seen concerning Mary from these statements of the various popes and from Vatican II:

1. She offered up Christ to Divine Justice
2. She offered herself up with Christ
3. She died with Him in her heart
4. She brings merit to men
5. She is a coredeemer of the human race with Christ
6. She distributes the grace, which has thus resulted
7. She was free from all sin
8. She was fashioned by the Holy Spirit into a kind of new substance and new creature
9. She untied the knot of Eve's disobedience
10. She was free from all guilt of original sin
11. She was taken up body and soul into heavenly glory
12. She was exalted by Christ as Queen of all
13. She is still interceding for men today
14. She still wins for us today gifts of eternal salvation

I had to conclude that as nice as all the above sounds to some, and as encouraging as they may think it is, it is not Scriptural. There is not one of the above statements that can be substantiated by Scripture. Many of them even contradict Scripture. Every one of these statements was formed and fashioned by the Roman Catholic Church.

Christ offered up Himself to Divine Justice---Mary was not involved. It is never stated in Scripture that Mary offered herself up with Christ on the cross. Nor does the Scripture even hint that Mary died with Christ in her heart. And she is never said to bring merit to men, nor is she ever called a coredeemer of the race with Christ. And without question, she is never said to be the distributor of grace, which has resulted from the work of Christ. And on and on we could go! It is all untrue according to Scripture!

About this time, I must admit, my heart was deeply stirred for the glory of the Lord Jesus Christ, and the Biblical truth that He was the one and only mediator between God and men. I realized that so many of those who exalt Mary are very sincere---but sincerely wrong! There is one mediator between God and man, and that mediator, the only mediator, is the Lord Jesus Christ (I Timothy 2:5).

But what we have just studied shows not only that truth, but the great necessity of the doctrine of Sola Scriptura! Is it not now crystal clear where fancy and human emotion can take us, if we are not anchored to Scripture? How easily we can come to the place where we would allow the contradiction of Scripture, even when it clearly states that there is one mediator between God and man?

Then just as I was about to nod off to sleep, the nurse came running out, and she called to me to come quickly, because Dink was giving signs of coming out of his coma.

I put my papers in my briefcase, and made a bee-line to the intensive care unit, and sure enough, Dink seemed to be rallying.

When he saw me, he smiled and said rather softly, but clearly, "Hey, Preacha! Show me dat pitcher a dat guy you says looks like ya!"

I smiled back with a tear or two in my eyes, and then replied with a smile, "Hey, Dink! You missed out on all the fun! Where have you been?"

He looked a little puzzled and shot back, "Maybe da better question is, where am I now an what happened ta me? An if I'se been out fer awhile, did ya solve da crime yet? Have ya caught da guy or guys who was tryin' ta frame ya? I hope ya don't need me too soon on dis case, cause I ain't feelin' so good, yet."

What Does the Bible Say?

It would have taken far too much time to tell Dink the whole story, and I knew he wasn't up to it, so I simply urged him to rest, and told him that in time I would bring him up to date. I also informed him that he had been unconscious for over a week now, but not to worry---we had caught the mystery man, and it was Todd.

After reading Scripture and praying with him, I stood by the bed till he had drifted off to sleep once again. Then I did the same (drifted off to sleep, that is) on the couch in the hospital waiting room! I wasn't the only one that night using the waiting room for a nap time. But the problem with keeping uncertain hours, and living on naps, is that the body comes to the time when it has no idea when it is supposed to sleep or be awake. Thus, one can easily become a night owl, awaking at strange and uncertain hours---especially when trying to nap on a hospital couch.

Thus, when I stirred about 2:00 in the morning, and couldn't get back to sleep, I figured I would occupy the time by my next step in the study of Roman Catholicism. But, first, some review. I had set forth the doctrine of Sola Scriptura, that is the doctrine of the Bible only as our authority. Second, I had compared it with the Roman Catholic Church's multi-source doctrine of authority (the Bible plus the pope's statements, plus the councils' decrees, plus tradition, plus, etc.). Third, I had shown how this multi-source authority treats a doctrine, using the doctrine of Mary as the example, and how a doctrine in the Roman

Catholic authority system becomes over the centuries far different than it was as recorded in the New Testament. Now, at this juncture, I wanted to show how, after the passing of many centuries, the doctrine of Mary had changed so dramatically, and how it now actually infringed on the life and ministry and glory of Jesus Christ.

I decided to do this by a series of questions, letting the Scripture answer each question (the underlining is mine).

1. **How many mediators are there between God and man?**

    For there is one God, and <u>one mediator</u> between God and men.   *I Timothy 2:5*

    The Bible never says Mary is a mediator of any kind!

2. **Who is the one mediator between God and man?**

    For there is one mediator between God and men, the man <u>Christ Jesus</u>...   *I Timothy 2:5*

    ...<u>He</u> [Christ] is the mediator of the new testament...
         Hebrews 9:15

    The Bible never says Mary is a mediator of any covenant between God and man!

3. **Who has obtained eternal redemption for us?**

    ...by His own blood He entered in once into the holy place, having obtained eternal redemption for us.
         Hebrews 9:12

The Bible never says Mary has obtained any kind of redemption for us, or that she had any part in that work of God for us!

4. Who has purged our conscience from dead works that we might serve the living God?

How much more shall the blood of Christ, who through the eternal Spirit offered himself without spot to God, purge your conscience from dead works to serve the living God. Hebrews 9:14

The Bible never says Mary has purged our conscience from dead works!

5. How many times is it necessary for Christ to die in order to make a payment for our sins?

...it is not often, as the high priest [Old Testament high priest] enters into the holy place, every year with blood of others, for then He [Christ] often have suffered since the foundation of the world. But now once in the end of the ages, has He appeared to put away sin by the sacrifice of Himself. Hebrews 9:25-26

So Christ was once offered to bear the sins of many... Hebrews 9:28

By which will we are sanctified through the offering of the body of Jesus Christ once for all. Hebrews 10:10

But this man, after he had offered <u>one sacrifice for sins</u> <u>forever</u>, sat down on the right hand of God.
                          Hebrews 10:12

For by one <u>offering He has perfected forever</u> them that are sanctified.   Hebrews 10:14

The Bible never says Mary made any kind of offering for our sins, or that Christ must be offered over and over again, as in the Roman mass.

6. **Where does the Bible teach that Mary was sanctified in the womb, and therefore without original sin?**

It doesn't!

7. **Where does the Bible say Mary's body never suffered the corruption of the flesh, but was taken to heaven, sparing her from remaining in the grave till resurrection day?**

It doesn't! This doctrine is admittedly an assumption!

8. **Where does the Bible teach that Mary has a maternal influence over God, so that she can turn away God's wrath, making her a mediatrix between God and man?**

It doesn't! The Bible teaches that Christ is the propitiation (the wrath ending sacrifice for sin) for all our sins!

9. **Where does the Bible teach that Mary can intercede for our sins?**

    It doesn't! As noted above, there is one mediator for sin, and that is the man Christ Jesus.

10. **Where does the Bible teach that Mary is the redemptrix of captives and the refuge of sinners?**

    It doesn't!

11. **Where does the Bible say that Mary has a powerful role in the redemption of mankind?**

    It doesn't! Christ is the only Redeemer!

12. **Where does the Bible indicate that we are to fear Christ, in that He is also God and Judge, to any extent, and/or that we should therefore have a subsidiary mediator in Mary?**

    It doesn't! Christ invited all who were weak and heavy laden to come to Him (see Matthew 11:28)! Neither He nor Scripture ever speaks of any unwillingness on His part to receive sinners!

13. **Where in the Bible are we taught to pray to Mary?**

    Nowhere!

14. **Where does the Bible say that Mary brings merit to men or that she distributes the grace of Christ to us?**

Nowhere!

So we could go on and on! The tragedy is not just that these doctrines are not in Scripture, but it is that these doctrines so often contradict Scripture in such important areas of truth! Even if one would allow other authorities besides the Bible, surely all the other individual authorities of a multi-source theology structure should not contradict the Bible, if both are from God! But when there is such contradiction between the individual authorities, which make up a multi-source authority structure, then it should be a clear warning to all that the multi-source authority structure cannot be God's true authority!

I looked at my watch, and by now it was about 4:00 AM. I figured I had better get another brief nap, before it was time to give the task over to the day shift! As I waited to fall thoroughly under the influence of sleep, I thought about the many positives the Roman Catholic Church thinks it has---its history; its historic cathedrals; its beautiful and impressive music; its reverent and stately ceremonies; its elegant vestries and adornments; its great theologians and supposed saints and holy men; its world-wide influence; its dominance in some places; its claim that it dispenses the merits of Jesus Christ to men, etc., etc. But what good are any of these things, if they do not teach the truth?

I also wondered how the Roman Catholic Church could ever judge itself, if it had become the judge and infallible interpreter of the Bible? Should not the Bible judge the church, instead of allowing the church to be the judge of the Bible or add other authorities to the Bible?

28

Who Is the Man Who Was in Jail?

As I left the hospital this Saturday morning, a little over a week after the explosion, my mind wasn't on much of anything---just to get home and go to bed. I wasn't even aware of the flashing light of a police car again, until the officer gave me a brief sample of his siren. I thought wearily to myself, "What now?"

As I looked into the rear view mirror, I discovered it was the same southern-talking officer who had had pulled me over previously. I wondered, doesn't he ever quit? His initial greeting wasn't very encouraging.

"Boy, you're in a bigger heapa trouble now! Follow my vehicle down to the police station!" he demanded.

My protests of needing sleep and rest didn't matter much to him. He was immediately in his "vehicle" again, and we were on our way. I couldn't even begin to imagine what he wanted now. And I wasn't in any condition of mind or mood to even try to imagine!

When at the station, my "Barney Fife" type of police friend led me into what must have been an interrogation room. With all seriousness he told me what he could so easily have told me when he pulled me over.

"We want you to know that your jailhouse friend we have had incarcerated here for the past several days has escaped!" he finally offered.

"He what?" I exclaimed, and then added, "And don't call him my friend! I am not sure who he is!"

"Well, anyway, he escaped---he's no longer in our jail here!" he explained sheepishly with some evident embarrassment.

"How in the world did he do that?" I asked.

"Well, you've got to understand that he's a pretty slick character!" he explained, trying to exonerate any responsibility the police might have had for the disappearance of a prisoner out from under their noses.

Then with further embarrassment, he tried to explain how the "prisoner" (he loved using police terms) "negotiated his way out of his cell in a manner beyond the control of his fellow officers."

"You mean he just walked out, when someone left the cell door open?" I asked.

"Well, not quite, but kind of," he admitted.

After a long drawn out explanation, which I had to pull out of him, he admitted that Todd had some how slugged a guard, when they were changing his cell, and then used the guard's gun to get out of the police station. He had then "commandeered" (his police word again) a police vehicle, and had made his getaway! I was assured that the police were on top of the situation, and they were confident that he would be back in jail very soon.

Then I figured out, that I had been brought down to the station to be grilled for awhile to see if I had any idea where they might find him. I was told they thought that if I was in partnership with him, I wouldn't like it that he had left me holding the bag, and I might rat on him. But when they saw my disgust at their thinking, as well as their ineptness in the handling a prisoner, they thought they had better let me go---which they did. But as I left the police station, they gave me a note, which said, "You thought I was Todd, didn't you?"

As I drove home from my unnecessary trip to the police station, I pondered what this recent turn of events might mean. If he wasn't Todd, who was he? Would the trial be postponed now until they found this guy, whoever he was? Wasn't he the essential witness in this case? Would that mean I would have this cloud of suspicion hanging over me indefinitely again? What if they never did find him?

But if I had thought the worst of the worst of this worst day had already taken place, I was in for a greater surprise. I had no sooner arrived home, and had crawled into bed without even eating breakfast, when the phone rang.

"This is Mac! I've got some shocking news for you!"

"If it's that Todd, or whoever he is, broke out of jail, I already have that news!" I offered out of my sleepy stupor.

"What? That is news to me!" he said with a chuckle.

"Well, what else could be so shocking as that?" I asked, beginning to emerge from my unresponsiveness.

"Well, are you sitting down?" Mac asked.

"Mac, I'm lying down!" I laughed in return.

"Here it is---the man in jail there was definitely not Todd! The remains of Todd were found yesterday in the forest and brush of the area where he had bailed out before his plane struck the mountain. Obviously, the body was decomposed after such a length of time, but they have just made a positive identification of him. I wanted you to be one of the first to know, before the news hit the papers. He probably died on impact, and never moved from the initial spot where he landed. The money was all there. And the identification is positive beyond any doubt!"

He added that he had no clue as to the identity of the man who had been in jail here in Seminary City. I thanked him for the information, and as I hung up the phone I pondered, "Where does that leave me now?"

29

What Is the Spiritual Condition of Man?

Since I had no idea who or where the mystery man was, I checked all my doors to be sure they were locked before I tried to go to sleep once again. It took me awhile to drift off, as there were so many questions buzzing through my mind. If the mystery man definitely was not Todd, who was he? Will we ever find out who he was? Could he change his identity once more? And why had he taken my identity, and pulled off such a scam, if it wasn't for revenge against me? Who was there in my past who would have wanted to frame me and ruin me, as much as Todd did?

After a restful day, I made my way back to the hospital once again, and the first thing I did was to fill in Dink on all the events he had missed while he was unconscious---even the latest concerning Todd's death and another jail break of my "twin." He began talking about checking out of the hospital, and getting on the case, which I discouraged. I realized, however, that it was just a matter of time before we would be looking for some answers.

When I returned to the waiting room, I decided to turn my attention to my theological pursuit. This time I was going to tackle the Roman Catholic Church's view of man. What is their view of man, and does it differ from that of Scripture?

The Roman Catholic View of Man

1. <u>Man in his original state</u>

Man in his original created state possessed considerable human powers---free will, an amazing and capable mind, and a viable conscience. But man at creation was also given other gifts, newer and higher gifts, which took him beyond the boundaries of his human nature---gifts which drew him into intimate familiarity with God and carried him beyond his natural state. Thus, every man, because of these preternatural gifts, which exceed all man's natural powers and needs, enters the world in relation with God.

2. Man in his fallen state

When man fell in the garden in Adam, he lost the preternatural gifts, but he lost none of his natural gifts, though they were weakened to some extent, but not totally. Man's will is still free, though somewhat weakened. Man's mind is still quite capable of understanding truth. Man's conscience still functions properly. Man does, however, have inherited sin---Adam's universal inclination to sin---which he inherited from the sin of the first man. Thus, each man's personal sin is derived from the sin of the Adam.

But beyond the sinful acts of all men, sin is a power which brings a three-fold death---death of the soul, death of the body and death in the form of damnation (the second death). Personal sin is a consequence of this. We might chart the Roman Catholic Church's view of man's condition before the fall as follows:

MAN BEFORE THE FALL

AFTER CREATION
Preternatural Gifts
Given to Man
as He Is Elevated
by Grace at Creation
/\
|
|
|
|

|
|
|
|

CREATION
Man's Natural State
Which Was Given
at The Time of His Creation
by God

We might chart the Roman Catholic Church's view of man after the fall as follows:

MAN AFTER THE FALL

Preternatural Gifts
Given to Man at Creation
Lost at the Time of the Fall

|
|
|
|
|
|
|
|
|
V

Man Falls Back to His Natural State
His Natural Powers Remain
Though Weakened

==

Man's Will Still Free
Man's Mind Still Capable of Understanding Truth
Man's Conscience Still Functions Properly
But Man Cannot Release Himself from Sin
Man Has Lost Grace
Man Has Lost the Principle of Supernatural Activity
Man's Condition from Man's Side Irreparable
Man by Natural Acts Cannot Make Things Right

Thus, according to the Roman Catholic Church, man
needs the grace of God, but at the same time he has the

ability to cooperate with the grace of God in Christ provided for him through the Roman Catholic Church. The fall did not leave him devastated and helpless, but only brought him back to a natural state, where he is somewhat impaired, but still able to cooperate with God's grace in salvation.

A Comparison of the Roman View with the Bible

We will let the Bible make the judgement once again, as we note the following verses, remembering what the Roman Catholic view believes about man, as stated above.

Ephesians 3:1
You hath he quickened who <u>were dead</u> in trespasses and sin

Clearly, we who are now Christians were once, as all men, spiritually dead in our sins. We have been delivered from the power of spiritual death, which became ours through Adam.

Romans 3:7-8
10 There is none righteous, no, not one
11 There is none that understands (spiritual things)
11 There is none that seeks after God
12 They are all gone out of the way
12 They are together become unprofitable
12 There is none that doeth good, no, not one
13 Their throat is an open sepulcher
13 With their tongues they have used deceit
13 The poison of asps is under their lips
14 Their mouths are full of cursing and bitterness

15 Their feet are swift to shed blood
16 Destruction and misery are in their ways
17 The way of peace have they not known
18 There is no fear of God before their eyes

Jeremiah 17:9
The heart is deceitful above all things, and desperately wicked: who can know it?

Thus, it is clear! All men are dead in sin! No man is righteous! No man understands the things of God! No man seeks after God! We are all unprofitable to God. Not one of us does any good! Our mouths are full of wickedness! We have not known the way of peace! Not one of us fears God!

Clearly, this is what man is within his natural state. Adam, as man's representative, forfeited man's relationship with God, and all mankind lost all favor with God! He brought mankind under the curse and power and condemnation of sin! When Adam sinned, all mankind became guilty and remains guilty before the holy God of heaven! Man is unworthy! Man is undeserving! Man is powerless to seek or know God except God seeks man and reveals Himself to man. Man deserves only hell and separation from God forever! Man has no merit whereby he can obtain grace or favor with God. Man has an enslaved will, a blind mind spiritually, and a corrupted conscience! His fall was a real fall and a deadly fall.

This Biblical view of man is clearly in strong disagreement with the Roman Catholic Church's view, which says the fall was only the loss of the preternatural gifts, as man only fell back to his original state of creation. But where does the Bible speak of the giving of preternatural gifts to man? Surely the fall described in the Bible left man far more devastated than man was in his original creation state. Again, we can chart the Biblical view as follows:

MAN BEFORE THE FALL

Man's Natural State at the Time of His Creation
================================

A Will That Is Free
A Mind That Is Capable
A Conscience That is Able
An Ability to Seek God and Serve God
A Life That Is in Fellowship with God

MAN AFTER THE FALL

Man's Natural State Given at Creation Was Lost
Which Included the Following
================================

Man's Will Is Now Enslaved
Man's Mind Is Now Blind Spiritually
Man's Conscience Is Now Corrupt
Man's Only Hope for Salvation Is the Grace of God
Man Has No Power within Himself to Earn Salvation
Man Is Enslaved in Sin and Will Continue to Be So
until God Moves upon His Heart and Life
by the Power of the Gospel

We cannot over-emphasize the importance of this doctrine, because we can never be right on the doctrine of salvation, unless we are correct on the condition of fallen man.

30

What? No More Heapa Troubles?

The rest of the night went by quite rapidly! Dink was gaining strength by leaps and bounds, and was now out of intensive care. He was bound and determined to be out of the hospital---very soon.   I discovered that with his improvement marching along so steadily, I needed to get a few things done that I had been putting off. I knew as soon as he was out, we would be absorbed with the investigations before us---to find the mystery man and to determine who he was, and in the process, clear my name.

I had been requested to make an appointment with Dr. Harbour, Dean of Faculty at the seminary, and so I did make one for that afternoon. I had no idea what he wanted, and I was still puzzled as to why no one from the seminary had been to visit Dink, but I guess I would soon find out. I made my way to his office at the scheduled time, and braced for whatever the appointment might hold. Dr. Harbour was very gracious and appeared glad to see me, and even disappointed that I had not come sooner. He began the conversation, after the usual greetings.

"Dr. Pointer, I want to share with you the good news that we have been given permission to reinstate you and Dink as faculty members. You have proven your innocence, even the falsehood of accusations brought against you by the mystery man. We are sorry for any inconvenience that this whole situation has caused you or your family! How soon do you think you can be back in the classroom teaching?"

He may not have meant for it to appear that way, but the question at the end of his statement caused me some concern. He wanted me back in the classroom teaching, but why? Was it that they were hurting for substitutes, and that was the reason he wanted me back so soon? Or could it be that he wanted to cover his error, as quickly as possible? He had jumped to the conclusion that I was guilty, when I was not. Had he so soon forgotten his total unwillingness to believe my strong protest of innocence, and that he would give me no opportunity to clear myself? My answer, therefore, was somewhat evasive.

"Well, Dr. Harbour, I am not sure if or when I am coming back to teach!" I was not just hassling him, but I meant it!

So I continued.

"Sir, I have not yet been cleared completely of the charges brought against me by the mystery man. Though he has disappeared, I must still settle some matters. It may be easier now, since my accuser just broke out of jail and disappeared. But I do not know what the officials may do! I think there needs to be some closure of this matter, before I do come back and teach. It seems clear now that I am innocent, but I do not want to go through what we have just experienced again, which could happen, if I came back to teach before this thing is settled for certain."

He was very understanding, and urged me to take all the time I needed. He assured me that the job would be open, after this was all settled, as he had promised. I thanked him, and then asked why no one from the seminary had been to the hospital to see Dink? He sheepishly agreed that was a major oversight, and that someone would see him today!

As I left the school to go on over to the hospital, my heart was rejoicing. A lot of uncertainties had just been settled! I still had a job, if I wanted it! I could still be teaching at the seminary---my choice! I did seem to be back in the good graces of my superiors, though it had not been any fault of mine that I was out of their graces! But then, all the euphoria was shattered by the blue light of my southern policeman friend, as he pulled me over for the third time in about as many days. I smiled, as I wondered what he wanted now.

He walked up from behind me, where he had parked, and said, without even greeting me, "Boy, the state's attorney's representative, working in this county, wants to see you right now! I hope you ain't in another one of yer messa heapa troubles! When you gonna settle down and do somethin' right?" he almost scolded me.

I smiled in return, and followed him, this time to the court house. I surmised that the state official hadn't even told him why he wanted to see me, but I began to think it might be good news. Wouldn't that shake up my "heapa trouble" policeman friend. And it was!!!

The state's attorney told me that all possible charges against me had been dropped! The case had been reviewed, and there was insufficient evidence to hold me in custody any longer. On my way out, I sauntered up to my policeman friend, and said softly with a smile, "Don't take this wrong, but I hope I never see you again! My heapa trouble is over, as far as the state is concerned! In fact it never should have existed." He was laughing, when I walked out the door.

But I still couldn't help but wonder where the mystery man was hiding out! Or if I would ever see him again.

31

Are We Justified by Faith or Works?

I went straight from the courthouse to the hospital, and shared the good news with Dink. He rejoiced with me, but still wanted to look into the matter when he was released from the hospital. Since he was now out of the intensive care unit, it was much easier to visit and stay awhile. So we had a good long talk, reviewing again all that had taken place. We stood amazed at God's grace and goodness to us, in guiding and protecting us through all the trials. And Dink was improving by leaps and bounds. They were even talking about letting him out soon.

After we had read Scripture, and even while we were still praying, the phone rang. It was Mac, and so I shared the good news of our reinstatement at school, and of my being cleared of all charges. He rejoiced with us over the great providence of our Lord. Then he gave me some news that really shocked me.

"They have a copy of Todd's will, and I obtained it. He named you the beneficiary of all his earthly possessions!"

"Me? Are you sure? There must be some mistake!" I blurted out with laughter. Then I remembered that there was another person who at least looked like me walking around in this world! But, seriously, why had Todd left me his inheritance? Me, of all people, after all the threats he had made against me?

Then Mac offered, "They say the inheritance is worth several million dollars!"

"Several million?" I blurted out again.

"But that's not all the news!" Mac offered again. "The mystery man was seen in California! It was a positive identification, but then he got away! They haven't found out his real identity, and have no idea where he might be now. But we're getting closer, and maybe his days of troubling you are almost over!"

After sharing these things with Dink, I walked back to the waiting room, so he could get some rest. I found myself repeating Mac's last statement---the days of the mystery man's troubling you are almost over! Would that ever come? Could everything soon return to normal? I sure hoped so! That was a nice thought, and I didn't mean to be a pessimist---only a realist! But the reality before me now was a continuation of my study of Roman Catholicism, and their view of the way of salvation.

Distinguishing the Various Views about Salvation

The way of salvation, as men seek to know God, expresses itself in one of three ways:

1. <u>Most religions teach a way of works in order for a man to be saved or to go to heaven</u>

   Man does certain things by his own ability and works, and he will be saved hopefully someday, as he continues to work and keeps on working. "Work and you will be saved" is the plan of salvation of this view. If there are no works, then there is no salvation. Salvation is the result of man's works. It is not that salvation results in man's works, but works are the cause of salvation.

2. The opposite of works salvation is grace salvation

This view says that salvation is completely by the grace of God, and that one cannot mix grace and works, or grace is no longer grace. This view says that godly works will follow salvation, not precede it. Man cannot work in order to save himself, in light of the fact that he is a condemned and helpless sinner in God's sight. Therefore, only grace can save him.

3. Then there are those who teach a way of salvation by a mixture of grace and works.

This view says that grace is available to man, but he must in some manner respond to that grace, and by his works through grace achieve salvation.

To summarize, we see the following:
1. Works alone as the way of salvation
2. Grace alone as the way of salvation
3. Grace and works mixed as the way of salvation

Distinguishing Two Views of Justification

A second question, which helps determine which one of the three views one holds concerning salvation, is to ask, how does a sinful man become just or righteous or acceptable in the sight of God? Does God make a man just and righteous, and then accept him because he is just and righteous? Or is it that a man is given the perfect righteousness of another, and thereby God declares him to be righteous because of the righteousness of that other person, and thereby he becomes acceptable to God?

The Roman Catholic View of Justification

Without going into great depths yet (we will later), it must be pointed out that the Roman Catholic Church view is that God infuses His grace into a man, and that man then does good works and performs good deeds, which make him acceptable before God. So in a sense, the Roman Catholic view can say, man is saved by the grace of God, but it is an infused grace, not an imputed grace. And it is only as the infused grace enables a man to do good works that he is acceptable to God. Man is acceptable to God because he is righteous within himself, due to God's grace and his own works.

But with this view there is always a question as to how many or how much good works a man needs to do to make himself righteous, so that he is acceptable to God. Can a man really possess a perfect righteousness on the basis of his own works, even performed because of infused grace?

This was what troubled Martin Luther. It was not just that he was a rebel against the church. He was seeking as a sinner to be acceptable to God. But he never had the assurance that he had done enough good works to give him the requirement of a perfect righteousness, which in turn would give him acceptance in the presence of God. No matter how hard he tried, or how much he did in the way of good deeds, or how faithful he was to the requirements of the church, he had no assurance that he was saved. He was continually tormented by the reality of his sin!

The Biblical View of Justification

The Biblical view of justification is that a sinner can never have a perfect righteousness of his own, because of the great depravity and reality of his sin. He can only have a perfect righteousness, if the perfect righteousness of the sinless Son of God can become his. The Scripture teaches that the perfect righteousness of the sinless Son of God can become his, even as a sinner, not on the basis of anything he can do, but by faith in the perfect life and death of the perfect Son of God. God imputes the perfect righteousness of Christ to him by faith.

One might illustrate it by the man who owes a billion dollars at the bank, a debt he could never pay. But another man has offered to pay it for him, if he will only believe that this one has offered and is able to pay such a debt. Thus, the man quits trying to pay his debt, but looks by faith to the one who will pay it. It is not that the other man offers to give the debtor all kinds of strength, so he can pay the debt. The debt is too great for him to pay! But it is, that when the man who is in debt accepts the payment of the other man for his debt, that the bank takes the money of the other man, and puts it to the account of the man who is the debtor. And it is marked on the debtor's account as "paid in full."

Christ, the Son of God, is the other man who alone could pay the debt of sin, and His perfect righteousness becomes ours by faith. That is imputation! Christ's righteousness imputed to us by faith! Thus, it is a legal matter! It is not experiential! There will be joy when one realizes the debt is paid, but the paying of the debt is the work of Christ for me.

Such a man, who has received Christ's payment for his sin, is changed in the experience of salvation, and that is regeneration. But regeneration or the change that takes place at salvation within a man is not the reason for his acceptance by God, for even though he is changed, he is not made perfect in reality, until he is in eternity. Yet still as a sinner by nature, he has been changed (regeneration), and he will continue to be changed (sanctification---that is, to become more holy in life), as he continues to live upon this earth as a Christian.

But none of that is the reason for his acceptance with God. His acceptance with God is strictly because of the righteousness of Jesus Christ---His perfect righteousness has been placed to my sinful account, and when God looks at me now, He sees the perfect righteousness of His Son, Jesus Christ, instead of seeing me.

Thus, to categorize the two views of salvation, one would have to say that the Roman Catholic view is grace and works, while the Biblical view is grace alone (sola gratia). But more on that later, as we will seek to give Biblical data for our claim.

Note these following statements of the Council of Trent, a council called in the mid-sixteenth century by the Roman Catholic Church to deal with the views of the Reformers (Both quotes are from Sess. VI, can. 11-12):

> If anyone says that men are justified either by the sole imputation of the justice of Christ or by the sole remission of sins to the exclusion of the grace and charity which is poured forth in their hearts by the Holy Ghost and is inherent in them; or even that the grace whereby we are justified is only the favor of God: let him be accursed.

> If anyone says that justifying faith is nothing else but confidence in the divine mercy, which remits sins for Christ's sake, or that this confidence alone is whereby we are justified, let him be accursed.

32

Where Is Mac?

I was hoping the next day would be a quiet one, since things seemed to be settling down. But it was not to be! Early in the morning Mac called once again.

"Dr. Pointer, the funeral for Todd is tomorrow, and then they will read Todd's will. I think you had better make a trip out here!" he insisted.

"Why do I need to come all the way out there to California? Just tell them I am not interested in the money! It's just money Todd made fleecing people in his unbiblical ministry! Tell them to give it to some good cause!" I replied.

"They can't do anything with it, without your signature. Besides, I have a hunch that the mystery man may show up at the funeral in some manner!" he informed me.

"What do you mean, in some manner?" I queried.

"He might show up as you---to get the money! After all, he looks like you, doesn't he? And talks like you?"

"Okay, if you insist! But you had better meet me at the airport, to give me protection from this imposter. Who knows if he might not seek to waylay me somewhere between the airport and the hotel, and try to pass himself off as me!" I said, trembling a little.

"Don't worry! I'll be at the gate to meet you! I will make you a reservation. Just call the airport and find out when your plane will leave later today. You can pick the ticket up at the airport, when you check in. Everything will already be paid for!"

I went to the hospital to see Dink, and clued him in on the new events, which meant I wouldn't be in to see him for a day or so. He wanted to go with me, but knew that was impossible. There was a possibility that he might get out of the hospital in the next few days, but it wasn't certain. So I told him I would see him when I got back.

I called the airport, and found out when my plane would leave. Then I went home and packed, and waited till time to begin the trip! There was one joy that I discovered in my travel---Mac had gotten me a first class ticket! He had hundreds of frequent flyer miles, so I crossed the good old USA in style!

It was about 9:00 PM when I stepped off the plane in California. There was only one thing wrong---Mac was not there to meet me! I began to consider quickly what that might mean. He was late? He had been waylaid by the mystery man? Or even worse, could it be that the imposter had already taken my place, and he was safely in my hotel room, with Mac thinking he was me!! I tried to tell my imagination that this groundless speculation was about to get out of hand, so just cool it! I sat down in the airport at the gate, waiting to see if Mac would show.

When he didn't arrive in the next fifteen minutes, I decided to call him, but only got answering machines. So I left several messages. Then I decided I had better go to the baggage carousel to get my suitcase. I found it waiting for me among some other bags. I was standing there trying to figure out my next move, when two men approached me.

"Dr. Pointer?" one of them asked.

I nodded, as I tried to assess this strange situation.

"Mac Turnover sent us to pick you up and take you to the hotel!" he informed me.

I was immediately suspicious. Mac had guaranteed me he would be there---in person! So I decided to ask a few questions, before going anywhere with anybody.

"Where's Mac?" I asked.

"He said he'd meet us at the hotel!" they offered.

"What hotel?" I asked, thinking they might give themselves away, in light of the fact I knew which hotel I would be staying in, and they might not know, if they were not sent by Mac.

"At the Sheraton!" one of them answered, giving the right answer, but not convincing me yet.

"Do you work for Mac?" I asked again.

"Sure! We've been some of his right hand men for several years!" they replied without batting an eye.

And then I got them. I asked them for Mac's phone number (I had them all). Surely, men who had worked for Mac for some years, as his right hand men, would know one of his phone numbers. They tried to appear confident, as they made some excuses for not being able to answer the question, and then one of them gave me a fictitious number. I knew then, I was not going to leave the airport with these guys! But what was I going to do?

Then one guy grabbed me by the arm, and the other stuck something solid in my back (I surmised it must be a gun), and he ordered me to walk with them---quietly. I surveyed the scene with my eyes, as my mind tried to decide what to do. I knew I must never leave the crowded area with them, or I was history. Then I saw the taxi stand about fifty yards away from me, and I bolted out of their grasp towards a waiting line of cabs, carrying nothing with me but my briefcase. They could have my suitcase---it might even slow them down. It must have taken them by surprise, as I saw that I had a pretty good head start on them, as I glanced over my shoulder

Then I thought, what will I do, when I get to the taxi stand? There was a long line of people waiting for a cab! Maybe I could play the part of a rude traveler, and jump in ahead of everyone and grab a cab and be gone! But then I realized if I tried that, the guys chasing me could be heroes by pummeling me before the crowd!

Then I spied two policemen near the taxi stand, and I headed towards them like a missile honing in on its target. As I burnt rubber on my sliding shoes, I almost slid into the police like a man going into second base. They looked at me with an "explain yourself" kind of stare, so I tried to introduce them to my problem.

"Those two men back there are trying to kidnap me, and they have a gun!" I said, panting for breath, as I pointed in the direction they should have been. But then, when they looked around to see the two men, they were gone! I tried to explain to the police that they were there a few seconds ago, and that they really had pulled a gun on me, but it made no difference. I figured I had better shut up and move on, but where to go was the question. I didn't dare wait in line, because the friendly thugs might still be watching and waiting to follow me. So I went back towards the airport itself, dodging people and luggage and vehicles, as I made my way in the opposite direction. Then I spotted a place where buses picked up passengers, and I made my way towards it. I boarded it not caring where it was going.

After traveling a number of miles, I spied a fairly nice looking motel, so I got off the bus, looking carefully, as I had been the whole trip, to see if anyone was following me. When convinced no one was, I darted towards the motel, checked in quickly, and then took refuge in my room, wondering what to do next.

I had to admit that things looked rather bleak! My clothes were gone! My nerves were shot! My contact man was nowhere to be found! And all I had was a briefcase, and a room in some part of California, and two thugs, who might even be standing just outside the door!

After peeping through the curtains to be sure no one was lurking about outside (I was on the second floor), I stretched out on the bed, trying to make some sense of all of this. Where was Mac? What time was the funeral tomorrow? How would I get there without Mac? Should I even try to go without Mac?

Some of my questions were answered, when I turned on the television set, and there right before my eyes was the picture of Mac. Immediately, I was glued to the TV set, only to be informed that Mac Turnover, the newspaper mogul, had been kidnapped, and no one knew where he was! It was also mentioned that the last time he had been seen was when he left for the airport to meet someone.

I could only conclude that the mystery man was the culprit, and he was also behind the men who tried to waylay me. He wanted neither Mac nor myself at the funeral tomorrow, or more importantly at the meeting for the reading of Todd's will.

It seemed right now, he was going to get his way!

33

Can a Believer Have Assurance
of His Salvation?

I decided I might just as well crawl into bed and do my thinking, I was so tired. As I did, my first thought was to go back to the airport immediately and get on the first plane home, whatever the price of a ticket. But then I knew I couldn't do that. I had to stay not only for Mac's sake, but also for what might be my last opportunity to find out who the mystery man was! When I couldn't go to sleep after thirty minutes or so, I decided to get up and do some studying. I was glad I had chosen to save my briefcase, rather than my suitcase, though most people might not understand that. After a few minutes, my mind was disengaged from the situation before me, as I sought to go deeper in my study of Roman Catholicism.

Infused Grace versus Imputed Grace

I noted in my thoughts, as I sought to resurrect my last study, that I had set forth the distinction between infused grace and imputed grace in the plan of salvation, as set forth by Roman Catholic Church and those who hold to Reformation theology. The Roman Catholic view says that God infuses grace into men, whereby they can then by His grace do good works, and therefore become righteous men and be accepted by Him. The Reformation view says that God imputes the righteousness of Christ to men by faith alone, apart from any works they can do, and on that basis alone God accepts men, whereby works follow by God's power, not to save men, but as the result of their salvation.

Thus, it should be easily seen that the Roman Catholic view fuses justification (man's being accepted by God) and sanctification (man's becoming righteous within himself). Justification and sanctification become one and the same. Thus, again, because of this false fusion between justification and sanctification, a Roman Catholic has a difficult time ever being able to say that he knows he is saved (accepted by God). Why, one asks, is this so? Because he must keep on working and hoping that some day he will make it, because his salvation in some way is based on his works and righteousness.

The Reformation view says that the two are separate. Justification is God accepting a man on the basis of his faith alone in Christ, even though he is a sinner, and the placing of the righteousness of Jesus Christ to his sinful account. Sanctification then is the work of the Holy Spirit within a man, after he has been justified (accepted by God on the basis of Christ's righteousness), whereby that man then grows in Christ, becoming more like Him in godliness and holiness of life. It is true that though justification and sanctification are distinct, on the one hand, one cannot separate the two. They cannot be separated in the sense that if justification has taken place, sanctification will follow.

But on the other hand, one must not, like the Roman Catholics, see the two as the same---man becoming righteous. Biblical justification is not man becoming a righteous man, but God declaring a man to be righteous, when he is not. He is declared to be righteous on the basis of Christ's righteousness, not his own. That declaration of righteousness (justification) is in an instant, when that man puts his faith in Christ. It does not take place within himself, but at the throne of God. Then, God by the Holy Spirit begins the work of sanctification, whereby the man begins to grow in righteousness, though he is still a sinner.

Thus, the comparison was complete, when we noted that according to the Reformation view a man can have assurance of his salvation right now, the moment he is justified before God by faith in Christ. The reason is clear! It is because his justification is not based on whether he as a man is righteous, but it is based on the perfect righteousness of Jesus Christ, becoming his by faith.

The Question of Assurance of Salvation

In further discussing this subject, we would ask a few questions. Does the Bible teach that a Christian today, as he lives on this earth, can possess the assurance of his salvation? Or, as it is often put, can a man know now that he is saved, that is, accepted by God? Can he know now that he has eternal life, when he comes to die?

For some this seems to be the epitome of pride. Some seem to think that if a man makes such a claim, he must really be deceived concerning himself to think that he is such a godly man that God would receive him. Surely, he must wait and find out if his life was good enough to merit such a claim. But if it can be shown, according to the Bible, that a Christian should be able to say that he knows he has eternal life now, that certainly should point us towards the Reformation view of justification and sanctification, as opposed to the Roman Catholic view. There is no doubt that the Bible speaks clearly on this subject!

1. 1 John 5:13

   These things have I written unto you that believe on the name of the Son of God; that ye may know that ye have eternal life,

   John the author of this epistle says clearly that we who believe on the name of the Son of God may know that we have eternal life. It is not a think-so, hope-so or maybe-so salvation, but a know-so salvation---because we trust Christ's perfect righteousness, not our own.

2. Hebrews 10:22

   ...a full assurance of faith...

3. 1 John 5:12

   He that hath the Son hath life; and he that hath not the Son of God hath not life.

   Salvation is wrapped up completely in Jesus Christ. If we have Him, we have eternal life. If we do not have him, we do not have eternal life. It is that simple! It is having His righteousness that God sees, when He looks at us, and not our sinfulness.

4. Romans 8:35-39

   35 Who shall separate us from the love of Christ? shall tribulation, or distress, or persecution, or famine, or nakedness, or peril, or sword? 36 As it is written, For thy sake we are killed all the day long; we are accounted as sheep for the slaughter. 37 Nay, in all these things we are more than conquerors through him that loved us. 38 For I am persuaded, that neither death, nor life, nor angels, nor principalities, nor powers, nor things present, nor things to come, 39 Nor height, nor depth, nor any other creature, shall be able to separate us from the love of God, which is in Christ Jesus our Lord.

If our salvation is by God's grace through faith in Jesus Christ, and if we possess a true faith in Christ (not just a church member or dependence on our works), then nothing can separate us from Christ!

5. 2 Timothy 1:12

For which cause I also suffer these things: nevertheless I am not ashamed: for I know whom I have believed, and am persuaded that he is able to keep that which I have committed unto him against that day.

The apostle Paul says that he is persuaded that God is able to keep him to the day of the appearance of our Lord Jesus Christ (see the context). Why? Not because of Paul's righteousness. He said in one place, that he is (present tense verb) the chief of sinners! (I Timothy 1:15) Yet, he is confident of his right standing before God!

6. John 10:27-29

27 My sheep hear my voice, and I know them, and they follow me: 28 And I give unto them eternal life; and they shall never perish, neither shall any man pluck them out of my hand. 29 My Father, which gave them me, is greater than all; and no man is able to pluck them out of my Father's hand.

There is no question about it!
    Christ's sheep hear His voice!
    He gives unto them now eternal life!
    They shall never perish!
    No man can pluck them out of His hand!
    His Father, who gave them to Him, is greater
        than all!
    No man is able to pluck them out of His
        Father's hand!
But on what basis? Only on the basis of the imputed righteousness of Christ to us.

Cannot a Believer Trust These Words of Christ?

I concluded that a believer couldn't be much more secure than that, and therefore he should be able to say now that he knows he is saved. And he can, as long as his dependence is upon Christ's righteousness and Christ's righteousness alone by faith, and not his works. But the moment his works are mixed in any way with grace or faith, he will always wonder if his works are sufficient, which will rob him of his assurance. I noted that we still needed to show that justification is by faith alone in Christ alone. But not tonight!

As I turned out the light and crawled into bed, it suddenly dawned on me, that I didn't know what time the funeral was or where it was! I had been dependent on Mac for all that information. But then I wondered if I dared to go to the funeral, or any of the procedures afterwards. Then I thought about a disguise, but how does one disguise himself without some help---makeup, a wig, etc. I didn't even have a hat or cap!

Then unexpectedly my cogitations were interrupted by a strong knock on my door!   That was the last thing I wanted to hear right now! Who could it be? Someone who was knocking on the wrong door by mistake? Or was it the thugs again?   I looked out the peephole, but couldn't distinguish who it was! I debated whether to open it or not. Why not just turn the lights off, and let them think no one was here, or that I was asleep.

But then what if they tried to knock the door down? Maybe I had better call the front desk and have them get some security officer to come to my assistance.

And then I heard a voice!!

34

Should I Go to the Funeral?

I have never been so relieved in all my life, when I heard that familiar voice, saying, "Hey, Preacha! Open da door! It's Dink!"

As I eagerly swung the door wide open, I had only two questions for Dink, and they came out automatically.

"Dink, what are you doing out here? And how in the world did you ever find me?" I asked with joyous bewilderment.

After we had hugged one another, and rejoiced together for several moments, he replied, "Well, Preacha! You'se knew dat I wanted ta come wid ya, an I guess I coulda. But, I figured I'd better wait till I was released from da hospital. So I sent an old buddy dat I trusted ta follow ya! I didn't trust yer imposter ta play by da rules. I figured he wuld try sometin' like dis. My buddy was on yer tail ever second of yer trip, even on da same plane! He saw dem boys try ta waylay ya, an he stayed right wid ya as ya ran away from dem. He saw ya try ta get da police ta help ya. An den he was on da bus wid ya, an saw which hotel ya went inta. When he contacted me, dey had just let me outa da hospital, and I had already heard dat Mac had been kidnapped, an so I was on da next plane, an here I is!"

I also learned that Dink had the name and address of the funeral home, and he knew where the will would be read. All we had to do now was go to sleep, and get some rest before the morrow. I must say, I certainly rested more comfortably now with Dink around!

We both were wide-awake early the next day. The television told us that Mac, the giant of the news business, was still missing, and the police were baffled! After a bite of breakfast we gathered our thoughts to try to figure out what our moves were going to be for that day. The funeral was at ten o'clock, and knowing the traffic would be horrendous, we checked out about 7:30 and took a cab across the city to the funeral parlor. We told the driver to stop in a place where we could observe who went in and out of the building without them seeing us

We saw no one we knew until about 9:45, when the mystery man showed up. He seemed to appear very confident, knowing Mac would not be there, but he must have wondered about me. I must confess that it was a strange sensation to see myself walking into the funeral parlor. At that point, Dink and I got out of the car and went inside also. When we noticed the imposter on one side of the hall, we sat on the other side.

As I looked around I noticed several things. Obviously, the casket was closed. Sadly, few people were in attendance. Todd's ex-wife was not there. The minister admitted, as he spoke, that he had never known Todd. Nothing good or bad was said about him, as there was just the reading of Scripture and prayer. I wondered what I would have said had I been invited to speak. I was probably the best friend he had ever known (until he went off the deep end theologically). Then he had no friends, because he wanted no friends, as he evolved into nothing but a self-centered ego-maniac.

When the funeral was over, I made it a point to stand in the certain sight of the mystery man. Finally, he saw me, but as he made a break for the door, the police grabbed him. I didn't know who had called them until Dink commented that his boys were right on time. As I had said many times, I said it again, if only to myself, that Dink has more contacts than the phone company.

After attendance at the graveside service, which was quite abbreviated also, as well as poorly attended, Dink and I made our way to the lawyer's office who was taking care of Todd's final affairs. It was then that I found out for certain that he was leaving me five million dollars! I told the lawyer I was going to give all the money away, because I had strong convictions against keeping it, in light of his final attitude of vengeance against me. I was convinced he had given it to me for some reason just out of spite.

The lawyer smiled, when I told him that, and agreed. He then presented the proof of my suspicion, as he read Todd's final statement addressed to me:

I send special greetings at this austere moment to my old friend and adversary, Dr. Ira Pointer.

I must admit that there is great uncertainty whether you will ever read or have read to you this final will and testament, in light of my plan of revenge against you. But just in case all my plans for you fail, I want you to know you have defeated me, and I have failed in my plan to destroy you.

But I want you to know that, as I promised, I did set in motion a set of events, which if they have gone well (well for me, that is), they should, in one way or another, destroy you and your ministry. My plan is to disappear with several million dollars, and yet leave the appearance that I may have perished in an airplane crash, though I bailed out before it struck the mountain.

If I survive bailing out of the plane, which will crash, leaving no evidence of my survival, I will seek to destroy you by becoming you by appearance, and by the publication of the book you no doubt know all about by now, if you hear these words. I will also have failed to bring about your death by an explosion in an apartment building, if you receive these words.

If I do not live, that is, if I perish as I bail out of the plane, I have paid another man very well, and I have trained him even better in your mannerisms and lifestyle. It will then become his duty to become you, and thereby destroy your life, one way or another, as described above. So you see, either way, you are targeted for destruction.

And if by some strange quirk of providence you survive, and all my plans for you fail, I am leaving you all my remaining estate, which should be quite substantial, in light of the great success I had, as the foremost end-time prophet of this era---until you destroyed me and my ministry. I want the world to see your phony and hypocritical life, as I am convinced you will be devastated by the love of filthy lucre in the passing of time. If not you, then your wife and children will become the curse of your soul in the years to come, as they succumb to the temptation of possessing so much money.

So, one way or another, my dear brother, I have set it up for you to be eaten up by the cancer of filthy lucre and worldly possessions, something you always warned me of and seemed to have conquered in your own life.

But I trust you will also fail, like I have, to heed the Biblical warning in I John 2:15 to "love not the world, neither the things that are in the world, for if any man loves the world, the love of the father is not in him."

By the way, in closing, let me say that you will never guess who the man is, who has become you, if it is not I. Let me assure you that you do know him, but could never guess who he will be. Or, for all you know, it may be me after all!

I sat almost lifeless, while the lawyer went through the other final procedures of settling his will. My mind went over the past, searching for someone I had known who would succumb to Todd's plan to try to destroy me. Who else in this life had I come across who had the maniacal and twisted hatred for me, so as to cooperate with Todd in his vengeful scheme against me?

At least I knew one thing! The mystery man was someone from my past! Someone I had known! Someone I had helped? Or was he someone I had offended, unknowingly?

When I turned and looked at Dink, he didn't even wait for the question, but simply whispered, "Don't ask me, Preacha! I ain't got da slightest idea. But at least, we knows dat da police got him now, unless he's escaped from dem already---again!"

I smiled! Escape again? Then where would we be?

35

Can Grace Ever Equal Works?

As soon as the legal matters were settled, I was met by a mob of Todd's relatives, from near and far. First, they sweetly and lovingly assured me that they would be glad to take the money out of my hands, since I had indicated I didn't want it. But then they began cursing and even spitting on me, when I told them I wanted to study the matter first, and pray about where the Lord wanted it to go. Only Dink's firm attitude delivered me from their wrath.

From the lawyer's office, Dink and I headed to the airport. We had several hours before our plane took off, but where else was there to hang out? But then we were further surprised when we got word through a television monitor at the airport that the mystery man had escaped again. They also said that Mac's captors had released him. I immediately made my way to a phone and called his number. The answering voice, evidently one of his aides, told me he was unavailable at the moment, but he had left word for me that he would call me when I got home.

When I got back to Dink, I got his commentary on the mystery man's latest escape, as he said, "Dat man's got more lives dan a dozen cats! But, dontcha worry, Preacha! We'll gets him yet! He's gotta be somebody we knows, accordin' ta old Todd."

By the way, I also had time to go to the lost and found to regain custody of my wayward suitcase.

The trip home was uneventful, except for the fact that it gave me time to take the next step in my theological study.

It was my desire to establish that the Scripture teaches salvation by faith alone in the work of Christ. To be honest, there were so many verses, I had a time deciding where to begin and then what verses to include in my study.

I chose the following verses to illustrate beyond any doubt that according to the Scripture a man's salvation is based not on his works, nor on a mixture of works and faith, but on faith alone in Jesus Christ and His work for us. All underlining for emphasis is mine.

1. The simplest question and the simplest answer--- salvation is by faith in Christ

   When the Philippian jailer asked what he should do to be saved, Paul replied:

   Acts 16:10
   Believe on the Lord Jesus Christ and thou shalt be saved.

2. The simplest question and the simplest answer expanded---salvation is by faith not by works

   Ephesians 2:8-9
   8 For by grace are ye saved through faith; and that not of yourselves: it is the gift of God: 9 Not of works, lest any man should boast.

   Romans 3:27-28
   27 Where is boasting then? It is excluded. By what law? of works? Nay: but by the law of faith. 28 Therefore we conclude that a man is justified by faith without the deeds of the law.

Romans 4:2-5

> *2 For if Abraham were justified by works, he hath whereof to glory; but not before God. 3 For what saith the scripture? Abraham believed God, and it was counted unto him for righteousness. 4 Now to him that worketh is the reward not reckoned of grace, but of debt. 5 But to him that worketh not, but believeth on him that justifieth the ungodly, his <u>faith is counted for righteousness</u>.*

Romans 5:1

> *Therefore <u>being justified by faith</u>, we have peace with God through our Lord Jesus Christ...*

Romans 9:31-32

> *31 But Israel, which followed after the law of righteousness, hath not attained to the law of righteousness. 32 Wherefore? <u>Because they sought it not by faith, but as it were by the works of the law</u>. For they stumbled at that stumblingstone.*

Romans 11:6

> *<u>And if by grace, then is it no more of works</u>: otherwise grace is no more grace. But if it be of works, then is it no more grace: otherwise work is no more work.*

Galatians 2:16

> *Knowing that a man <u>is not justified by the works of the law, but by the faith</u> of Jesus Christ, even we have believed in Jesus Christ, that we might*

> *be justified <u>by the faith of Christ</u>, and <u>not by the</u>*
> *<u>works of the law</u>: for <u>by the works of the law</u>*
> *<u>shall no flesh be justified</u>.*

Titus 3:5-7

> *5 <u>Not by works of righteousness which we have</u>*
> *<u>done</u>, but according to his mercy he saved us, by*
> *the washing of regeneration, and renewing of*
> *the Holy Spirit; 6 Which he shed on us*
> *abundantly through Jesus Christ our Saviour; 7*
> *That <u>being justified by his grace</u>, we should be*
> *made heirs according to the hope of eternal life.*

Can any reader honestly dispute the teaching of Scripture, when it says that faith alone is the way of salvation, and that faith is the gift of God, and that salvation is not by works or the law?

What Saith the Roman Catholic Church?

I would ask the reader to consider the statements of the Roman Catholic Church concerning the subject. All of the following statements are taken from declarations made by the Council of Trent in the sixteenth century, the church council called by the Roman Catholic Church, as they sought to answer the beliefs of the Reformers at the time of the Reformation.

1. <u>Statement One of the Roman Catholic Church</u>:

> *If anyone says that men are justified, either by the*
> *sole imputation of the justice of Christ or by the sole*
> *remission of sins, to the exclusion of the grace and*

*charity which is poured forth in their hearts by the
Holy Ghost and is inherent in them; or even that
the grace whereby we are justified is only the favor
of God: let him be accursed. (The Council of
Trent, Sess. VI, can. 11-12)*

Note carefully what the Roman Catholic Church is
saying here:

If anyone says one of the following:

a. If anyone says that men are justified by the sole
    imputation of the justice of Christ, let him be
    accursed.

    This says we are not justified solely by the
    imputation of the righteousness of Christ, which
    is a direct contradiction of Scripture.

b. If anyone says that men are remitted of their
    sins to the exclusion of the grace and charity,
    which is poured in their hearts by the Holy
    Ghost and is inherent in them, let him be
    accursed.

    This states the Roman Catholic Church view of
    infused grace and charity, which are poured into
    our hearts by the Holy Spirit, which then works
    with the grace which is inherent within us, so
    that we can do good works to be saved.

c. If anyone says that the grace whereby we are justified is only the favor of God, let him be accursed.

This states that salvation is not by the grace or favor of God alone, but something must be added to His grace, whereby we can be saved.

I ask again, does this not clearly contradict the statements of Scripture, which we have just noted previously in this chapter? I would urge the reader to read them again in the preceding pages!

2. <u>Statement Two of the Roman Catholic Church</u>

If anyone saith that justifying faith is nothing else but confidence in the divine mercy, which remits sin for Christ's sake, or that this confidence alone is whereby we are justified: let him be accursed. (Ibid.)

Note what the Roman Catholic Church is saying:

a. If anyone says that justifying faith is nothing more than confidence in divine mercy, which remits sins for Christ's sake, let him be accursed.

This states clearly that faith alone in the mercy of God to us in Jesus Christ and His work on the cross for us is not enough to save us. Evidently, something more than the work of Christ for us has to be added. And what is that? The works of man! Thus, salvation is a mixture of faith and works, something the Bible says (as we have seen) cannot mix!

b. If anyone says that this confidence in Christ alone is the basis of our justification, let him be accursed.

Again, is this not saying that justification is not by faith alone in Christ alone? If justification is not by faith in Christ, then it must be by works or a mixture of faith and works, which we have seen is not scriptural.

3. <u>Statement Three of the Roman Catholic Church</u>

If any one saith that the justified, by the good works which he performs through the grace of God and the merit of Jesus Christ, whose living member he is, does not truly merit increase of grace, eternal life---if so be, however that he depart in grace---and also an increase of glory: let him be accursed. (Ibid., Sess. VI, can. 32)

a. This states clearly that a man performs good works through the grace of God and the merit of Christ, and thereby he merits an increase of grace, even eternal life.

It is true that this states that the good works which bring a man eternal life are performed by a man through the grace of God and the merit of Christ, but it is still by the works of man. From this statement one wonders where faith in Christ is to be found in this statement of salvation.

b. This states that all of man's performance of good works only remain in effect to save him, if he departs this life in grace. If he does not depart this life in grace, he does not have eternal life. Clearly, all depends on man's works!

4. <u>Statement Four of the Roman Catholic Church</u>

Life eternal is to be proposed to those working well unto the end and hoping in God, both as a grace promised to the sons of God through Jesus Christ and as a reward which is, according to the promise of God Himself, to be faithfully rendered to their good works and merits. (Ibid., Chapter XVI)

a. Life eternal is proposed to certain ones

to those working well unto the end
to the ones hoping in God

This is another statement that salvation is a mixture of grace and works, and that it is not by faith alone in the work of Christ for us.

b. Life eternal, according to the Council of Trent, is proposed to certain ones on a two-fold basis.

Basis One
as a grace which is promised to the Sons of God through Jesus Christ

Basis Two
as a reward which is according to the
promise of God Himself, which is to be
faithfully rendered to their good works
and merits

This says the same thing as the previous statement, only adding a few more ideas. Life eternal again comes on the basis of grace promised to us through Jesus Christ and also as a reward for man's good works and merits based on the promise of God.

I had to raise the same question, which we had faced before, at this point. Why is there such a wide distinction between what the Bible says on this subject and what the Roman Catholic Church taught at the Council of Trent and teaches even today? Could it not be for the same reason we had seen above, that is, because the Roman Catholic Church's authority structure gives tradition, the statement of church councils, papal statements, etc., an equal authority to the Bible? Thus, they cannot read the simple statements of Scripture, taking the Bible as their sole authority, but they must mix in centuries of unauthorized authorities. Has this not in the passing of years changed the Biblical doctrine of salvation from a salvation by grace through faith in Christ to a salvation by a mixture of grace and works?

And even further, in light of their stated beliefs, what does the Roman Catholic Church do with Romans 11:6, which says that if salvation is by grace, then it is no more by works, for then grace is no more grace? And if it is by works, then it is no more by grace.

36

Is Not Faith without Works Dead?

Dink slept most of the plane ride home, and that, no doubt, was good for him. The last two days had put quite a strain on a body, which just a few days ago was near death. I was drained also from the two days, and I was closer to my normal health than Dink was. When I had finished my study, I put aside my books and laid back, and asked myself, who the mystery man could possibly be.

As we started our descent to land, Dink stirred and said, "Hey, Preacha, I just figured out who da mystery man is!"

Looking at him with a doubtful smirk, I challenged him, kiddingly, "If you're so smart, then tell me so I can be smart too!"

"Soon as I'se got da proof, I'll tell ya!" he offered.

"Does that mean you do or don't know who he is?" I asked again.

"It means I knows, but I ain't got da proof yet!" he said again.

"Then how can you be sure you know, if you haven't got any proof?" I said, laughing.

I couldn't tell if he was serious, when he answered with a smile, "Wait an see, Preacha! Wait an see!"

I carried the jest one question further, when I said, "Then how will I know that you knew, if you don't tell me now what you know?"

I wondered if I had irked him, but he replied with a confident smile, "Wait an see, Preacha! Just wait an see!"

I didn't want to admit it, but Dink had stirred my thinking, as I pondered the question for the next few hours. Who could this mystery man possibly be?

Meanwhile, after some deep sleep in my own bed, I found myself right back into my study, seeking to answer the most frequently asked question by the Roman Catholic laity concerning faith and works: "What about James?" I wish I had a dollar for every time someone had asked me that question when I was witnessing to him concerning salvation by faith without works. I had to admit that this was a good question, which had caused men confusion down through the ages; therefore, I had to deal with it

Introduction

We must admit that James at first appearance seems to contradict Paul's view of justification by faith without works in the following verses (again the underlining is mine):

James 2:17-26

17 Even <u>so faith, if it hath not works, is dead, being alone</u>. 18 Yea, a man may say, Thou hast faith, and I have works: shew me thy faith without thy works, and I will shew thee my faith by my works. 19 Thou believest that there is one God; thou doest well: the devils also believe, and tremble. 20 But wilt thou know, O vain man, that <u>faith without works is dead</u>? 21 Was not <u>Abraham our father justified by works</u>, when he had offered Isaac his son upon the altar? 22 Seest thou how faith wrought with his works, and <u>by works was faith made perfect</u>? 23 And the scripture was fulfilled which saith, Abraham believed God, and it was

*imputed unto him for righteousness: and he was
called the Friend of God. 24 Ye see then how that
by works <u>a man is justified, and not by faith only</u>.
25 Likewise also <u>was not Rahab the harlot justified
by works</u>, when she had received the messengers,
and had sent them out another way? 26 For as the
body without the spirit is dead, <u>so faith without
works is dead also</u>.*

I PAUL'S VIEW OF JUSTIFICATION, FAITH, AND WORKS REVIEWED

A. Paul's view of justification reviewed

Romans 3:21-22
    justification is apart from works
    justification is by faith
Romans 3:24
    justification is freely by His grace alone
Romans 4:3
    justification is by faith alone
Romans 4:5
    justification is to him that works not
Galatians 2:16
    justification is not by works but by faith
Galatians 2:21
    justification is not by keeping the law (works)
Galatians 3:11
    justification is not by keeping the law (works)
Titus 3:5
    justification is not by works of righteousness
       which we have done

B. A statement of the heart of the problem between James and Paul

The heart of the problem is that James and Paul use the same three words---justification, faith, and works, but the question is, do they use them with the same definitions?

Several years ago the importance of the meaning of words in their context (something I already knew) was driven home to my thinking in a dynamic manner. It was a sign in Britain at a rest stop on an interstate highway, as I was travelling, that jostled my sensibilities anew. The sign said: "Football Coaches Not Allowed!" I was half weary and almost worn out from travelling, but my brain asked the question, "What do these people have against football coaches---the likes of Tom Landry, etc." I couldn't figure it out, though I should have been able to do so.

That afternoon I was in a store and came upon a large bin of soccer balls, but the sign over them said "footballs!" Then I had to conclude that football means soccer in Britain. But then I asked, "What do Britishers have against soccer coaches?"

The next day we were traveling down the highway ---their interstate type again---and my driver said, while looking into the rear view mirror, "That coach is really coming around us fast!"

I looked up to see a bus go whizzing by, and I realized he had called the bus a coach, and my puzzle was solved---soccer equals football in the British context, and a coach equals a bus in their context! I was then able to translate their language into my English as follows---soccer buses were not allowed in their rest stops! Then I remembered the stories of the soccer hooligans after soccer games trashing places, and it all made sense.

I think that is the problem we have here as James and Paul use the same words, but in a different context, and therefore with different meanings. The words are faith, works, and justification.

C. Greater elaboration on Paul's doctrine of justification, faith and works

1. The problem that concerns Paul is man's guilt before God---man's lack of righteousness

   1:18   the wrath of God is revealed against man
   1:32   the judgment of God is upon man
   2:1   man is inexcusable before God
   2:2   the judgment of God is upon man
   2:3   do not think that you can escape the judgment of God
   2:5   man treasures up wrath and judgment
   2:8   God's indignation and wrath are against man's sin
   2:12   man will perish
   2:16   a day is coming when God shall judge the world

3:19   every mouth must be stopped from excusing man of his sin and all the world must admit its guilt before God

2. <u>The solution that concerns Paul is for a man to have a right standing before God (justification)</u>

see Romans 3:21-4:25
> the word righteousness is used twelve times
> the word imputed is used eleven times
> (λογιζομαι)
> thus the justification of man or declaration of righteousness which concerns Paul is before God and has the following characteristics:

imputed	positional
legal	not inward
outward	not subjective
non-experiential	not experiential

this means that justification
> does not take place within a man but at the throne of God
> is not an experience but something legal and declarative by God
> is based not on something within man which he has done, but something done for him by another---something done for him by Jesus Christ at the cross as He died and paid the penalty for our sins

3. <u>The solution of which Paul speaks concerns</u>
    <u>justification before God by faith</u>

    see the above verses in the previous chapter
        for proof of this statement
    understand also that Paul's definition of faith is
        the act of the whole man

    <u>faith includes the **mind**</u>---faith has a mental
        aspect---see Romans 10:17---faith comes
            by hearing---but faith is more than
                just head knowledge
    <u>faith includes the **emotions**</u>---faith has an
        emotional aspect---see John 16 concerning
            conviction of sin, as conviction lays bare
                a man's sin to his understanding and
                    as conviction brings a burden
                        of sin
        see Acts 16 concerning the conviction of the
            Philippian jailer as he was deeply moved
                and troubled in his emotions
    <u>faith includes the **volitional** aspect</u>---faith
        includes the will of man---not that the will
        can act of its own strength, but that true faith
        includes the will as one is enabled by the
        power of God to cast himself upon the truth
        of God by faith, which the mind has heard
        and understood, as the emotions have been
        stirred as well to see the importance of the
        message of man's sin and God's salvation
        through faith alone in the sacrifice of Christ
        alone

4. <u>The solution Paul speaks of is a justification before God apart from man's works</u>

This means that salvation is not produced by man's works, but saving faith precedes salvation and true Christian works follow

Works do not precede salvation with faith being secondary, nor is there a combination of faith and works preceding salvation

Faith precedes salvation and true Christian works follow

This does not mean that faith can exist without works, for true salvation will produce true Christian works but Christian works will not produce salvation

The proper Biblical order is
faith brings salvation which produces works

The proper Biblical order is not
works produce salvation
neither do works and faith together
produce salvation

Thus Paul's view concerns
justification before God
justification by faith
justification apart from works

II JAMES' VIEW OF JUSTIFICATION, FAITH AND WORKS

If we take Paul's definition of these three words, i.e., faith---justification---works---and place them on James, we will be faced by a contradiction in the Bible---the Word of God. But that is not possible!

A. James is concerned about a justification or a declaration of righteousness before men

Was not Abraham our father justified (declared to be righteous) by works when he had offered Isaac his son on the altar?

Abraham was saved by faith and declared righteous before God much earlier in his life than the above statement and context.

see Romans 4:3
Abraham believed God and it was counted unto him for righteousness.
see James 2:22
Do you see how faith wrought with his works, and by works was faith made perfect?
by works faith was consummated
by works faith was brought to its end
by works faith was brought to its goal
by works faith reached its full
development
by works faith was brought to its
culmination
thus James is not saying that Abraham
was saved by works or by faith and
works
rather James is saying
that Abraham's saving faith, which had
given him standing before God, was
brought to the end intended by God as it
produced true Christian works

thus works did not add to his salvation or
faith, but they proved the reality of
his faith and his justification before God
this was the concern of James also in 2:25
in the case of Rahab the harlot

B. James is concerned with a false faith which is only mental assent rather than the full-orbed faith

Thou believest that there is one God; thou doest well; the devils believe and tremble.
James 2:19

in this context James uses the word faith
in a one-dimensional aspect
the aspect of mental only
but he notes that this kind of mental faith
is not enough for even the devils believe
in that manner and tremble
that is they have a mental knowledge of God
but they have no conviction of sin
and they have never surrendered to God

C. James is concerned with works as the true proof of one's faith

The works which James speaks about are true
Christian works which are the result of true faith
not works done for the merit of salvation

As proof of this note the following verses:

14 What does it profit, my brethren, though a man say he has faith, and have not works (true Christian works).

17 Even so faith, if it has not works (true Christian works) is dead being alone.

18 I will show you my faith by my works (true Christian works).

20 But will you know, O vain man, that faith without works (true Christian works) is dead?

21 Was not Abraham our father justified (declared righteous before God) by works (true Christian works), when he had offered Isaac his son upon the altar?

22 See how faith wrought with his works (true Christian works), and by works (true Christian works) was faith brought to its end.

24 You see then how that by works (true Christian works) a man is justified (declared to be righteous before men), and not by faith only.

25 Likewise also was not Rahab the harlot justified (declared to be righteous before men) by works (true Christian works), when she had received the messengers and had sent them out another way?

26 For as the body without the spirit is dead, so faith without works (true Christian works) is dead also.

Thus the conclusion is that James and Paul use the same words, but define them differently as they are speaking to different needs in the church. Paul is speaking concerning how one is accepted by God, and James is speaking of the evidence in one's life who has already been accepted by God.

A CHART SUMMARY

WORD	PAUL	JAMES
Justification	before God	before men
Faith	true full-orbed	uses both meanings of faith ---mental assent and the true full-orbed faith
Works	of the law to gain merit before God	true Christian works as evidence of one's salvation

When I finished, it hit me! I knew also who the mystery man was---not by proof, but by strong implication!

37

What Meaneth
the Roman Sacraments?

I put my books down and called Dink to see if we both had come to the same conclusion concerning the mystery man. He came on the phone with his usual "Hey, Preacha!"

I didn't return any chitchat or normal greetings, but told him immediately, "Dink, I've got it figured out!"

"What's ya got figured out, Preacha?" he returned.

"I've got it figured out who the mystery man is!" I informed him.

"Okay! You git Terry on da phone, an I'll git Janie. We'll both of us tell da wives da name of da mystery man, an den day can share da information wid one anudder ta see ifs we'se agrees!"

After doing as Dink suggested, Terry turned to me and said, "You and Dink agree on the identity of the mystery man!"

I got back on the phone with Dink and asked him what brought him to such conclusions concerning the mystery man.

"Well, Preacha, it ain't dat difficult! Todd says dat you knows dis guy well! Plus, he has ta be some guy dat is da same size, height an build as you! He, also, probly is some guy dat had some sorta grudge against ya! Plus, dis guy was a mystery man fer a few days before in our run-in wid him! Dat only left one guy dat fits da bill---Alfred Benjamin Newberry! Who else?"[1]

My mind went back to our last effort to solve a strange mystery, as it all began when Alfred Benjamin Newberry, better known as Pastor Newberry, walked into my office, and shared a concern, but then left without giving his name. And though we found him later, and though he wasn't guilty of the crimes he discussed with me, the whole thing resulted in several people leaving this world. In the process of the whole episode he became a very bitter man (he didn't have very far to go, as he seemed to have been a bitter man before we met him). As it all ended, he had to leave his pastorate, and the last we heard from him was that he and his family had moved out west somewhere.

Dink was right! He was my size and build! He probably left with a grudge against me, blaming me for the loss of his church! But how did he get involved in this diabolical scheme with Todd? And how had he become so adept at escaping from the police? And how would we ever find him now?

I called Dink back to ask him that final question. He informed me that he had already located Mrs. Newberry and had just gotten off the phone with her. She said her husband had left her almost immediately after they left Newberry, and she hadn't heard from him since. He had become a different man---moody, cranky, bitter, unable to hold a job, blaming others for all his problems, especially me. She said she finally had to tell him to leave, which he eagerly and readily did. She hadn't seen him or had any communication from him since he left. She had no idea where he was, or where he might be, and she didn't care to ever see him again!

"Well, what do we do next?" I asked Dink, rejoicing that I wasn't having to make these decisions alone, as I had been doing, while Dink was missing in action.

"Preacha, I don't tink we hasta do mucha anyting! You'se gots what he wants---da money. Da only way he could git his hands on it would be ta take it outa da bank, claimin' ta be you, or by blackmail in some manners."

"I guess I had better give warning to the bank of the possibility of someone wanting to withdraw any of the money. And, wow! Don't you think I had better take extra precautions to protect my family?" I asked, as a pang of horror shot through me!

After some time of discussion with my family, warning them of special precautions to take, and after a time of prayer with them, I turned back to my meditations on the Roman Catholic Church.

The Foundation Laid Thus Far

1. In my study I had emphasized thus far the importance of the doctrine of Sola Scriptura---Scripture alone as our authority. I had argued that this doctrine will keep a person anchored to the truth of Scripture, and is far less likely to allow one to wander off into falsehood, which is based on other supposed authorities that men would seek to add to our authority structure.

2. I had also compared the simple beliefs and practices of the early New Testament church with the Roman Catholic Church at the time of the Reformation, and had asked, how did anyone move from here to there? That is, how did that which was the true New Testament Church move from the simple New Testament doctrines and practices in the first century church to the beliefs and practices of the Roman Catholic Church as seen at the time of the Reformation?

3. In answer to that question, I had demonstrated the changes which took place in several doctrines of the New Testament, as they evolved through history, when other sources than the New Testament began to guide the church. Some doctrines even came to the point that they contradicted the New Testament teachings, though the Roman Catholic Church would never admit that. The doctrines I had noted were the doctrine of Mary and the doctrine of salvation.

4. I especially noted the contradiction which came concerning the doctrine of salvation. The change which took place was a move from salvation by grace alone through faith alone in Christ alone, as taught in the New Testament, to a mixture of grace/faith and works, as taught by the Roman Catholic Church at the time of the Reformation. I had shown where the Scripture declares unarguably that any attempt to add works to grace nullifies grace, and it is no longer grace but works (see the verses in Chapter 35, especially Romans 11:6).

The Corresponding Change
in the Ordinances/Sacraments[2]
Which Took Place

It will be our argument in this section that once the doctrine of salvation changed in the passing of the history of the church from grace through faith in Christ alone to one of works, the New Testament view of the ordinances or sacraments changed in the passing of history also.

1. Prior to the doctrinal change in church history concerning salvation, there were two and only two

ordinances or sacraments---baptism and the Lord's supper. I would assert this on two grounds.

a. I argue this conviction based on the evidence of history. A careful study will show that the Roman Catholic understanding of seven sacraments developed through the history of the church. The Council of Trent listed the following seven sacraments: baptism, confirmation, Holy Eucharist, penance, extreme unction, orders, matrimony. The same number had been given by the Council of Florence in 1429. This number had been offered to Gregory X at the Council of Lyons in 1274. According to some writers Otto of Bamberg was the first who clearly adopted the number of seven in 1139. Even various Roman Catholic writers and theologians agree that the number of seven sacraments was not established until the middle of the twelfth century.[3] Thus, it seems clear that the early church had only two ordinances or sacraments.

b. The above argument, which we have just stated, lays the groundwork for a second argument for the existence of only two ordinances or sacraments. If the Roman Catholic view of the seven sacraments was late in development in church history, and not fully established until the twelfth century, then one must ask, how many sacraments or ordinances did the early church practice? Thus, it would be a proper argument that a sacrament or ordinance is an observance that the church is commanded to observe in the New Testament and expected to repeat in obedience to our Lord. From this understanding, we draw the conclusion that the number of sacraments or ordinances was two.

We are clearly commanded and expected to repeat the ordinance of baptism, as the introductory rite of the one professing faith in Christ as His Lord and Savior (Matthew 28:19-20).

We are clearly commanded and expected to repeat the ordinance of the Lord's Supper, not to add anything to our salvation, but to remember our Lord's death and show that death until he comes (I Corinthians 11:26).

2. The stage is now set to present another argument concerning the changes which took place in the first twelve centuries of the church. We would now contend that there was a parallel between the number of ordinances, changing from two to seven during this time, with the change in the doctrine of salvation from grace alone by faith alone in Christ alone to a grace/faith and works plan of salvation.

Is it not understandable that a church with the conviction that salvation is not by grace alone brought to us by Christ through faith alone, must have some other means of communicating grace to mankind? And did that means not conveniently come to pass in history in the form of the Roman Catholic sacraments, for the sake of establishing an absolute dependence upon a growing, central, exclusive, all-powerful, absolutely necessary church? This was the period, remember, when the Roman Catholic Church was seeking to dominate the world religiously and politically! This was the time when the Roman Catholic Church established the idea that there was no salvation outside their church!

Thus, the Roman Catholic Church could not allow the teaching of salvation by grace alone through faith alone in Christ alone, but it had to build a superstructure of belief and practice, which tied their constituents to the Roman Catholic Church for salvation. The church alone could distribute salvation, through the merits of Christ and the sacraments. The church had to put fear into men's hearts that they could not separate themselves from the church, lest they forfeit all hope for salvation. And it cannot be denied that this is what the church did! And though Vatican II has softened these convictions somewhat, still many Roman Catholics today live under that belief and threat and fear that to leave the church is to forfeit one's soul.

I would challenge the reader to couple all of these changes in doctrine and in the sacraments with the barbarian invasions of the fifth and tenth centuries, which we have already discussed.

3. I was now prepared to take a quick look at the Roman Catholic view of the sacraments. They bind a person to the church from the cradle to the grave, and beyond, never giving a final certainty of salvation, but always giving (supposedly) a little more grace needed for a some day hoped-for salvation.

BAPTISM brings regeneration or supernatural life to a person.

CONFIRMATION brings spiritual strength and growth to a person.

THE EUCHARIST furnishes spiritual food and nourishment.

PENANCE heals the soul which has been wounded by sin.

EXTREME UNCTION removes the last remnant of human frailty from a person and prepares the soul for eternal life.

ORDERS supplies ministers to the church, and thus this is not a sacrament for all members of the church.

MATRIMONY gives grace necessary for marriage and for the ability to rear children in the love and fear of God. This sacrament, obviously, is not for all members of the church.

4. But even at death the Roman Catholic Church offers no definite hope of eternity with Christ immediately, except for a few.[4]

   a. The souls of the just who die free from all sin go directly to heaven.

b. The souls of those who die in the condition of personal grievous sin enter hell, which lasts for all eternity.

c. The souls of the just who, at the moment of death, are burdened with venial sins, enter purgatory, which is the place of temporal penal purification. Here they face purifying fire until they are free from all guilt and punishment, at which time they are received into the bliss of heaven.

It must be added that it is well known that there are various means and ways of obtaining merit for oneself or for a departed loved one, whereby the time in purgatory may be shortened.

My argument should be clear to the reader: that the Roman Catholic Church's system of salvation is a far cry from the simple and comforting teaching of Scripture, that salvation is by the grace of God alone through faith alone in the work of Jesus Christ alone for us at the cross of Calvary, and the statement of Paul that there is one mediator between God and man, and that one is Christ Jesus our Lord. The church has been given for our benefit, but not for our salvation, nor can it be the mediator of our salvation, nor the distributor of the grace of God to us! The ordinances/sacraments have been given for our encouragement, but not as the means to make us Christians or bring us salvation.

I could not help but weep for those who live throughout their lives with no assurance that at death they will go to be with Christ. I sat rejoicing with Paul's clear statement, that to be absent from the body (for the one trusting Christ), is

to be present with the Lord (see II Corinthians 5:8).
Though he said in the next verse, that he labored to be
accepted of Him, his meaning was not that salvation is by
works. We have already seen his view on that matter. But
he labors to give proof by his life that he does possess the
salvation, which has been given by grace, and which
salvation will always produce true Christian works.

My thoughts were interrupted, as usual, by a ringing
telephone. The voice I heard simply stated, "This is your
mystery friend. I want to see you and talk to you face to
face!"

---

[1]See the tenth book in this "journey series" titled *A Journey in Baptism*
(Richbarry Press, Columbia, SC), 2002.

[2]Baptists and many other groups use the word "ordinances" in
reference to baptism and the Lord's Supper, stressing that they have no
saving power, but are only symbols of Christ's work for us, which is
the basis of our salvation. Other groups, such as the Presbyterians, use
the word "sacraments," but do not give baptism and the Lord's supper
saving efficacy. Roman Catholics use the word sacraments in reference
to their seven sacraments, and give to these sacraments the power of
giving men the grace of God through participation in such sacraments.

[3]This is noted by S. Lewis Johnson, Jr., in an article titled "Mary, the
Saints and Sacerdotalism" in the book *Roman Catholicism*, edited by
John Armstrong (Moody Press: Chicago), p. 129. Johnson footnotes
the claim with reference to the Roman Catholic theologian Ludwig Ott,
Fundamentals of Catholic Dogma) 1974, p. 338.

[4]Ludwig Ott, *Fundamentals of Catholic Dogma*, Translated from the
German by Patrick Lynch (B. Herder Book Company: St. Louis), pp.
475-485).

38

Where Shall We Meet?

I was rather shocked to hear the mystery man calling, and had not anticipated what to say on such an occasion. Should I tell him that we knew or that we had a strong suspicion who he was? Or should I play along with him to see what he wanted. I decided to follow my first idea.

"Sir, I think you are using words rather loosely, because you have not been in the last few weeks a friend, but neither are you a mystery man any longer!" I informed him.

Silence followed my initial thrust. It was so silent one could have heard a feather falling through the air, and the time element was so long before he replied, that one could have heard it hit the ground as well.

After he had regrouped, he replied, "That is just a ploy to get me to expose myself! I assure you that you do not know me!"

"That's not what Todd said in his will, which was read after his funeral! He said when we find out who you are, we would be surprised, because we do know you! And he was right!" I continued to play with him.

The silence was so strong, that I wondered if he had hung up on me, though I had not detected any click. Finally, he spoke again.

"All right! So you know who I am. That doesn't change anything! I still want to talk to you face to face! You owe me a piece of that money!" he said, showing his greed.

"How should I address you when I see you?" I pressed him further. "Should I call you Pastor Newberry? No, that wouldn't fit any more, would it. Should I call you just Albert Newberry? Or do you prefer the full name of Albert Benjamin Newberry? Or maybe just Albert or Mr. Newberry would do? And what is your address? I'm sure your wife would like to have it, don't you think so?"

I knew I was pressing his buttons pretty hard---maybe too much so! But sometimes the shock method works---especially in a situation like this! When he didn't answer, I changed my tone.

"Look, I don't mean to irritate you, but what happened to you when you left Faircastle last year? Did that whole event leave you this bitter?"

Still I heard no click, indicating he had hung up. There was only what seemed to be a dead line. But I kept talking!

"Think of your family! Think of your wife and kids! What good could any part of this money that Todd left to me do you? And what happened to your professed relationship to the Lord? Or your claimed commitment to the ministry? I will be glad to meet you face to face, but I hope we can talk about you and your future---not the money!"

He answered, but his voice had softened, when he said, "Dr. Pointer, you always make so much sense when I talk to you, but I never seem to listen to you, do I? You were the one who talked me out of my revenge on the Kingston brothers there in Faircastle. But I gave you a fit over your trying to help me there, didn't I? And, now, look what I have done, and even what I was about to do! When can we meet? But more importantly, what can I do to make amends for what I have done?"

"You name the place! I'll be there!" I answered.

39

Why Are Men Drawn to a Church?

I called Dink to tell him that Albert Newberry had agreed to meet with me (he had said nothing about Dink coming or not coming). He wanted to meet me at 4:00 that very afternoon in a vacant house where he was staying in a town about ten miles out of Seminary City. I was glad Dink was going with me. He knew more about the ways of the criminal mind.

After I told Terry the seeming good news, I decided I had time to put the final touches on the notes for my book. Though there was so much more that could be said, I wanted to close with some answers to the growing number of Protestants who were considering becoming Roman Catholics, thinking they had found something there that they have not found in evangelical Protestantism. True, I could have cited multitudes, whom I had known over the years, who had left the Roman Catholic Church, but that was not my purpose. I wanted to answer some of those who had left or were thinking of leaving Protestantism.

1. Some think they find in the Roman Catholic Church a stronger basis of <u>authority</u> than they find in Scripture alone.

    We have already dealt with this issue, but a few more words are needed. One needs to ask if there is not some relationship between the recent battle over the Bible, which robbed many minds of the inerrancy of the

Scripture (in its original manuscripts), leaving themselves with an uncertain authority. Thus, another uncertain authority would not be so illogical in these minds, leaving them open to the acceptance of the uncertain authority of tradition, etc. It seems it would be very difficult, for one who holds firmly to the inerrancy of Scripture, to be open to an equal authority of some other source.

What I am saying here is that one must ask, if those who have left Protestantism for the Roman Catholic Church (or are considering doing so) did not do so from the foundation of a weak view of the Scripture? Is one leaving a weak authority (an errant Scripture from their view) to add another weak authority (tradition, etc.), or is one seeking to add a weak authority (tradition, etc.) to an inerrant Scripture as one's authority base? Again, it would be quite difficult to add tradition, etc., to a strong view of authority, which holds to the solid concept of Sola Sciptura---a view based on the verbal inspiration of Scripture, which gives us an inerrant and infallible Bible.

2. Some consider going to the Roman Catholic Church because of an apparent <u>unity</u> they think is found there.

It has been said that Protestants are so splintered and fractured into such small groups, which are so independent, that they are even (many of them) independent of God. How inviting the Roman Catholic Church appears to many! It presents a worldwide, seemingly monolithic community, with a strong hierarchical infallible church! It possesses a visibly recognized and revered pope as leader (who is respected by many who are not even Christians, as the leader of Christianity in the world). It has universal beliefs, and an appealing liturgy, and a ministry that includes not only the spiritual, but also the concern for men's social needs as well. And further, it is argued, did not Christ pray that His people might be one, even as He and the Father are one (see John 17:11)?

Yes, that is true, but the question one must ask is this: Was Christ praying for a visible earthy structure of unity as found in one denomination, which has in it some who are His own and some who are not? Could there ever be a true unity of such a visible structure? Or was Christ praying for a spiritual oneness of all His true people, regardless of their fellowship with some local church or national denomination or worldwide organization? Is there to be found anywhere a local church, or a denomination, with a pure membership, which would be the necessity of a visible unity?

Was not our Lord praying for a spiritual unity, which He must bring---not a unity of size or power or money to impress men, but a spiritual unity over which He rules His people in an invisible worldwide manner? And though they never meet together for worship and prayer or ministry, still He rules over them for they are His invisible church, His spiritual body, His people, His own. Could we not be looking for something to impress men, when we long for a large, world-wide, visible organization, rather than the true unity that is found only in His true spiritual body?

3. Some have, it seems, a rather <u>romantic</u> reason for looking to the Roman Catholic Church.

This would include the reverence for the long history of the church (though it does not go back to Christ, as the Roman Catholic Church claims). But that very claim, as false as it is, intrigues some. Then there are the ancient and magnificent cathedrals. What a comparison they can be to the little Bible-believing churches, which often (not always) meet in a school, or in a store-front building, or in a trailer park somewhere, or in a run-down, ramshackle rented house on the other side of the tracks in almost every local community.

In these churches the liturgy is lacking, the dignity is questioned, the awesome reverence of the magnificent cathedral is absent, and the music is not performed with professionalism and precision. Many often smile upon such places as substandard in comparison to the great cathedrals and the Roman Catholic worship practices.

But might we not do well to remember that the early church met in homes and caves and hidden places at times, and their worship practices were not necessarily according to the standards of some today, and yet their worship was acceptable to God? Again, may it not do us well to remember that it is not the place, nor the professionalism, nor the liturgy, but it is a matter of the heart that is acceptable to God. Forms are proper in worship, but not if the heart is not right with God. May we never give more importance to the outward forms than to the inward condition of the heart, as we come to worship God. May we never be so enamoured with the atmosphere, that we think that an aesthetic experience is all we need.

This is not to jettison the ancient or the aesthetic or the historical or the romantic, but it is a warning not to make it the whole of our emphasis in picking one church over another. We must worship God in Spirit and truth---not in a special atmosphere or aesthetic feeling or some romantic awe. Worship in Spirit and truth needs to be the emphasis and plumb line for our worship---we must worship in the Spirit and according to the truth of God's word.

4. Some, no doubt, have a <u>theological</u> reason for looking to the church of Rome

This comes back (usually but not always) to our basis of authority once again, so we have traveled full circle. My theology determines my authority or authority structure. But there are also cases where one's love for and belief in a certain doctrine or practice influences his choice of an authority structure which will allow that doctrine or practice. We must admit that some pick one church, because they agree with it in some area of important thinking, and then this helps them (maybe not immediately but over time) determine their authority structure.

For example, let one become enamoured with a doctrine which is found in the Roman Catholic Church, and one would then be open to the Roman Catholic Church's multi-source of authority, because it will allow that doctrine.

Thus, again, we find ourselves facing the key issue---what is one's authority structure. The choice of Sola Scriptura leads a person in one direction, as we have seen, that is, maintaining the Biblical doctrines. The choice of a multi-source authority, leads in another direction, that is, to an evolving theology which leads to many additions and sometimes subtractions from New Testament truth.

I looked at my watch, and discovered that it was time to get ready to go get Dink and head the ten miles out of town to meet Albert Newberry. As I drove to pick up Dink, I couldn't help but think how the mystery man fit into my discussions.. Albert Newberry was a man who had made a profession of faith in Christ. He had been baptized to testify of his faith in Christ. He had surrendered to what he thought was God's call to him to become a pastor. He had pastored for a number of years at several churches, the last one being the First Baptist Church of Faircastle. Yet, when I first met him he was carrying a revengeful spirit against the Kingston brothers for killing his father, and for their part in disinheriting him from the family as a baby. He was seriously considering taking their lives, because of their sin against him and his father, even though he was a preacher.

He didn't commit any crime, but out of the context of events which followed in Faircastle, he left his church, went west, and then squandered a large inheritance. The inheritance came because he found out that he was a child of the Kingston family---that is, a brother to the men he had wanted to eliminate from this world, because of what they had done to his adoptive father. The family had given him away when he was young, so they wouldn't have to rear him as their own. He became a very bitter man with a revengeful spirit, who had no joy, and then he left his family to become involved in this whole mess of events planned by Todd against me.

I remembered once again that it is not being a member of any certain church, nor is it attendance at any certain church, nor is it the ordinances or sacraments of any certain church, nor is it being part of any certain denomination, which brings one acceptance with God. But it is true faith and faith alone in Christ, which saves us. But we must add, such a true saving faith, will be evidenced by the living of a holy and godly life.

There will be multitudes of Baptists, and Presbyterians, and Methodists, and Roman Catholics, etc. who will spend eternity separated from God in a place called hell. And it will not be because of the lack of a church, or church works, or Christian ordinances, etc., but because they do not know Jesus Christ by faith in His person and work at the cross of Calvary for sinners. We have already seen that such a person can know he or she is saved for eternity---not by works, but by faith in Christ!

Thus, the questions I would want the readers of my book to ask themselves would be these: Am I really a true believer in Christ? Am I depending on Him and Him alone to save me? Or am I depending on something else---the church, the ordinances or sacraments, good works, etc? Is my profession of faith in Christ really evidenced by the presence of a holy and godly life?

These questions must be answered by all who profess to be Christians---Roman Catholics, Baptists, etc. A man or woman does not go to heaven because of a relationship to a church, but because of a saving faith in Jesus Christ alone!

40

What Is the Question
for the Mystery Man?

Dink was waiting for me when I drove up to his house. I immediately asked him, in light of the thoughts I had just written, what he thought of Albert Newberry's supposed change of heart?

"Well, Preacha, ta be honest wittchya it could go either way! It depends on whether ere not he's ever really been saved. He could be anudder Todd---an initial seemingly true profession a faith, but da more he lived, da more he gave evidence dat he had never been changed by da power of God. It was one false ministry after anudder. Till finely he destroyed himself, proving he'd never really been saved! Der just wasn't any true Christian works---I don't care how much he said he waz saved---his life never did show it!"

He continued his theologizing (he didn't know what I had just written).

"Now Albert Newberry seems ta be goin' down da same road. Good beginning, den nuthin but stumblin' along da way, an now a clear turnin' point. He's at a crossroad, dat may well prove whether he's ever been saved. A true faith is gonna produce true Christian works, but up ta dis point, da jury's still out. Da question now is dis: which way's he gonna go? Will he begin ta give evidence dat he's been truly saved, or is he gonna evidence dat he only made a false profession of faith in Jesus, which looked good, but dat don't stand da test a time. Dat is not ta say dat works now is gonna save him, but dat if he does possess true salvation, den true works is gonna evidence dem selves or his profession wasn't worth a plug nickel!"

I thought to myself, when Dink had finished, that this is a difficult concept for some men to understand, but it is not difficult if one will understand this much:

1. At salvation one is accepted by God through His grace, which comes to the person through faith and trust in Jesus Christ and what He has done for one at Calvary.

2. But also at salvation we are regenerated (made a new creature---II Corinthians 5:17), and all things become new in Christ. What we could not do, that is, change ourselves, though we had tried for years to change ourselves time and again, God did in an instant.

3. Thus, we receive two things at salvation: (1) acceptance with God on the basis of faith in the finished work of Christ for us, whereby His perfect righteousness becomes ours and gives us a perfect standing before God; (2) an inward change, wrought by the power of the Holy Spirit, which will give us the power to live the Christian life.

4. It was not the inward change, however, that made us righteous inwardly in a perfect manner, whereby God can now accept us. This cannot be true for two reasons. First, we are already righteous men before God, as He sees us, for when He looks at us, He sees Christ's perfect righteousness, which became ours by faith. Secondly, such a perfect righteousness can never be produced by us, no matter how long we may try.

5. Yet, at the same time, it was God's purpose to make us righteous men inwardly. But now, after we have been saved, we have the foundation whereby we can begin to grow in righteousness, not to be saved or add to our ability to be saved, but to produce a practical daily righteousness. This work is called sanctification, and it continues to make us more like Christ all of our lives.

6. But, again, what if one says he has been saved, but there is no change in his life after his profession? What if there is no growth or advancement in the Christian life? What if there is no Christ-likeness? What if one stumbles and struggles in the Christian life, never giving any evidence of a godly life, but lives the same life which he lived before, with all its same problems and sins. What if such a one still continues the claim of having been saved, and advances such a claim in the cloak of a supposed Christian life and setting?

7 Again, we are looking for a faith which trusted Christ for salvation, which was accompanied by an initial radical change, and then a life that continues to grow in Christ-likeness and the fruit of the Spirit---love, joy, peace, longsuffering, meekness, kindness, temperance, faith, etc. We are not looking for perfection. It is true that every Christian will struggle with sin as he lives (see Romans 7), but it is one thing to struggle with sin and another thing to be the continual slave of sin.

Those are the questions for Albert Newberry. Is his a true faith, which gave him standing before God, which then was evidenced in a true Christian life? Or has his life been only a pattern of enslavement to sin?

41

Is It All Over Now?

I turned off the main highway, as Albert Newberry had instructed me, and made my way down a narrow street to its end. The house he had indicated in his instructions was a rundown white house that needed not only a paint job, but also plenty of other repairs. When we pulled into the driveway, such as it was, with its chug holes and deep ruts, there was no sign of life on the premises.

Carefully and cautiously we made our way to the front door, which was about to fall off its hinges. As I tried to open it, it creaked as it swung half way open, before it was blocked by the floor of the porch. I knocked on the door, but no one answered. I began to wonder if we had been set up again by Albert Newberry, but then he appeared, not at the door, but from around the side of the house. He invited us to follow him to the back door, but by the time we had descended the front steps and walked to the corner of the front of the house, he was nowhere to be seen. I wondered again what kind of game he was playing.

I looked at Dink and asked him if he thought we should follow a man we could not see at the moment. He acknowledged that he wasn't sure, but then he started walking slowly down the side of the house, and I reluctantly followed. Maybe there was nothing to fear, but in light of the events of the past few weeks, I found myself very uneasy about the circumstances before us.

When we reached the back of the house, Dink stopped me right at the corner, as he took a look around it.

"I don't see nobody, Preacha!" Dink said, still surveying the scene in the back yard.

"Shall we try knocking on the back door?" I asked.

Dink shook his head as he continued to study the matter.

Looking around the corner over Dink's head, I saw an old building in the yard about the size of a small garage, and the door was open.

Concluding that was the probable route Albert Newberry could have taken, I suggested we look in the garage.

Again, Dink shook his head, as he looked around the yard for something. He found an old two-by-four out in the high grass at the side of the house, and brought it back to the corner where I was standing.

"Preacha, I wants ya ta stay behind dis corner. I'm gonna trow dis two-ba-four inta da garage, an I'm gonna hit da ground right witchya. Ya got dat?" he asked.

I peeped around the corner while he stepped out into the yard a few feet, and then he threw the two by four towards the garage in an arc. But as soon as it left his hand, he pushed me back and fell on top of me just around the corner, as a terrible explosion took place! When all the debris and rubble had fallen, we got up and peeked back around the corner, and the garage was gone---except for a pile of boards, etc. on the ground.

We then walked towards the ruins, and began sifting through them to see if someone had been in the building when it exploded. And then we saw it---the remains of a body! And though it was not a pretty sight to behold, it was beyond doubt the remains of Albert Newberry!

By that time several police cars had pulled up, along with a fire truck. Dink and I found ourselves trying to explain the whole situation, which was not an easy task. After going to the police station to make out a full report, and after calling our wives to tell them we were okay, Dink and I started home.

"Well, I guess Albert Newberry either changed his mind about wanting to straighten out his wrongdoings," I observed, "Or he never had any intentions of doing so. All he wanted to do was to die and to take us with him! That means he died with the same spirit of revenge driving his heart at his death, which had driven his heart throughout his life for so many years---which does not speak well of any profession of salvation which he made, earlier in his life, or even a few hours ago!"

"Yeah, Preacha, he had a trip-wire at da door an wanted ta take us out! I figured he'd slipped out a back door, but fer some reason he jus' wanted ta take us wid him! Sad!"

"I guess that ends any threat Albert Newberry or Todd Shelton might be to us in the future!" I added with a sigh of relief.

"I hope you'se is right, Preacha! I hope you'se is right!"

I didn't quite know what he meant by that statement, but I wasn't in any mood to pursue it further today. Todd Shelton had plagued me for more years and in more ways than I wanted to remember, and Albert Newberry had contributed to my grief these past few weeks, as much as any man could over such a short period of time.

As far as I was concerned, the question of their salvation was very strong! They had given clear evidence that, though they were preachers, and though they had professed to know Jesus Christ, their lives testified exactly the opposite. Again, I had to note that being a Baptist or a Methodist or a Presbyterian or a Roman Catholic is not

220---A Journey in Roman Catholicism

what saves a man. Only knowing our great God through Jesus Christ His Son, and only trusting in the sacrifice He made at Calvary's cross for us will save us. Church works, church rites, church membership, church blessings---none of these things can save, for the church does not have the power to save! God through Christ is the power to save, and the church is only the signpost that should point to Him. How sorrowful that so many think that they can ride the signpost to heaven, when Jesus Christ, to whom the signpost is supposed to point, is the only One who can save them! How sorrowful also that so many churches think that they are more than a sign post, and that in some way they have the power to save men!

Scripture is clear when it speaks of the relation of Jesus Christ to our salvation:

Neither is there salvation in any other:
for there is no other name under heaven given among men,
whereby we must be saved (Acts 4:12)